THE PRINCIPLES OF DAIRY FARMING

THIS BOOK IS DEDICATED TO THE

MEMORY OF MY FATHER

WHO FIRST AROUSED MY INTEREST

IN CATTLE

The Principles of
DAIRY
FARMING

by
KENNETH RUSSELL
B.Sc., N.D.A. (Hons.), N.D.D. (Hons.)
Late Principal, Shuttleworth College,
Biggleswade, Bedfordshire

Revised by
KEN SLATER
M.Sc. (Newcastle) B.Sc.Ag. (Hons Dunelm)

FARMING PRESS LTD
WHARFEDALE ROAD, IPSWICH

First Edition	*1953*
Second Edition	*1954*
Second Impression	*1957*
Third Edition	*1962*
Fourth Edition	*1967*
Fifth Edition	*1969*
Sixth Edition	*1972*
Seventh Edition	*1974*
Second Impression (with amendments)	*1976*
Third Impression (with amendments)	*1977*
Fourth Impression	*1979*
Eighth Edition	*1980*
Ninth Edition	*1981*

© FARMING PRESS LTD 1953, 1980, 1981
ISBN 0 85236 116 5

This book is printed in Great Britain in 10pt on 11pt Times on Silverwhite Cartridge paper by Page Bros (Norwich) Ltd, Norwich

CONTENTS

CONTENTS

CONTENTS

CONTENTS

ILLUSTRATIONS

ILLUSTRATIONS

ILLUSTRATIONS

FOREWORD

By **SIR HAROLD SANDERS**

Formerly Chief Scientific Adviser (Agriculture),
Ministry of Agriculture, Fisheries and Food

TWENTY-SEVEN years have passed since this book was first published, years which have seen many and great changes in dairy farming. But the book has kept pace and this eighth edition brings it right up to date.

Since Ken Russell's sudden death in 1967 the contents have been modified and expanded initially by Stephen Williams and more recently by Ken Slater to cover all the new science and the new methods that have appeared. Agricultural sciences and the ingenuity of farmers seem to advance at an ever-increasing rate, but Ken Russell kept up with all developments. He had the rare ability to interpret science to farmers. It was no wonder that he was in such demand as a speaker at gatherings of farmers, and his writings have the same clarity of exposition as his lectures had.

His book deals with dairy farming in that down-to-earth manner for which he was renowned. When he describes scientific principles they do not seem difficult to comprehend, and when it comes to practicalities no doubt is left as to how the job should be done. In his years of teaching experience he kept abreast of agricultural sciences, but he always delighted in doing farm work himself and from his own experience gave specific directions how best to do it. It is all here in his book: theory and technique, skills and the personal qualities which are compounded in stockmanship. The last revision was carried out by Ken Slater; there have been many developments in dairying during the seventies and an attempt has been made to incorporate these in to the book without losing sight of the basic dairying concepts.

'Principles of Dairy Farming' is now thoroughly established in agricultural literature and the present edition lives up to the superlative standard of its precedessors. For the student it is, of course, quite essential reading, and it has very much to offer, in stimulus and information, to all who are engaged in producing milk. Throughout there is due and proper emphasis on profitability, the aim and object of the whole business.

H. G. SANDERS

Wollaston,
April 1980

PREFACE

(To Eighth and Ninth Editions)

During recent years there have been many advances in the field of dairy husbandry and management. These have been brought about by the rapidly increasing pressures on the dairy farmer, largely due to the escalating costs of dairy production.

Many of the recently introduced techniques have been included in this edition of the book. Above all, it is hoped that the reader will appreciate how the basic husbandry systems in the future must be related to prevailing economic factors. Only in this way will the dairy industry of the future have any hope for a continuing and profitable existence.

I am indebted in my revision of this book to my colleague Gordon Throup who provided the content of chapter 18, and also to John Hughes, Bill Thickett and John McArthur for their help and advice.

KEN SLATER

"There is a sede that is called discretion and if a husbandman have of that sede and myngle it amonge his other cornes they will grow moche the better."

FITZHERBERT
"Boke of Husbandry" (1523)

CHAPTER 1

THE MILK INDUSTRY

MILK as a food provides practically all the ingredients necessary to promote and maintain life. As our knowledge of the requirements of the human diet has increased, so the value of milk has been more fully appreciated. In times of war this has led to a considerable emphasis being placed on the usefulness of milk as an important feature of the diet.

In modern times, however, there has been an explosion in the use of convenience foods, so the consumption of milk per head in the United Kingdom has dropped from 2·75 litres per week per head in 1954–5 to an estimated 2·56 litres per week per head in 1980–1.

In 1976 consumed liquid milk accounted for 60 per cent of the total estimated production of milk in the United Kingdom. It has been estimated by the Milk Marketing Board that by 1979–80 this proportion had dropped to 48 per cent, the remainder being used for manufacture, that is, the production of butter, cheese, condensed milk, dried milk and fresh cream.

Marketing of Milk

The milk industry as a whole is divided into two main parts: the production of milk on the farms on the one hand, and the manufacturing and distribution of liquid milk on the other.

The marketing of milk is the essential link between these two divisions and is organised by five marketing boards operating in the United Kingdom.

Prior to 31 December 1977, there was a guaranteed price for milk linked to a 'Standard' Quantity or the total of milk sold off farms, whichever was the less. If the total sales of milk in any board area exceeded the board's standard quantity, the excess was claimable from the Government at the average price it earned on

15

the manufacturing milk market. These sources constituted the total sum of money to which the board was entitled. In the event of the board's total receipts from the market failing to reach its guaranteed price, the Government made up the difference in the form of a subsidy.

Abolition of Guaranteed Price
Following the end of the guaranteed price system on 31 December 1977 the marketing boards now obtain their income entirely from the market place for milk used for liquid consumption and manufacturing purposes. The marketing boards have to meet all the numerous charges such as administrative costs, advertising, sales promotion and milk transport from this income. The net sum remaining after these factors have been taken into account is payable to the producers at monthly prices which the boards prescribe.

These prices reflect a seasonal pattern of milk output within each board area and they relate to a specific compositional quality, with deductions or additional payments being made for milk which comes below or exceeds the basic class of milk for the area.

There are also deductions for a capital levy and the EEC co-responsibility levy.

The maximum price at which the boards may sell milk is fixed by the Government. These prices may be varied through the year if changes are made in distributive margins or the retail prices of liquid milk.

The prices of milk for manufacture are negotiated periodically between the creamery proprietors and the appropriate board. Milk prices are decided for each type of product. Through the year as market prices and milk available for manufacture rise or fall, so adjustments are made to the agreed prices and to the income which a board may expect to accrue by the end of a year.

Table 1.1 shows the relative distribution of income and expenditure for milk in the United Kingdom.

MILK PRODUCERS—REGISTRATION

Any farmer who wishes to produce milk for sale must first obtain permission from either the Ministry of Agriculture, Fisheries and Food, or local authorities, according to where in the United Kingdom he intends to start production. Once authority has been given, the producer is expected to comply with the regulations concerning clean milk production. The intending producer must then register with the appropriate Milk Board.

Table 1.1 Income and Expenditure for Milk in the United Kingdom

April to March 1979–80

	pence per litre
Retail price consumers paid for pasteurised milk	26·243
Distribution margin	12·470
Distribution allowances	0·263
Total distribution costs	12·733
Net returns for:	
liquid milk	13·510
manufacturing milk	11·015
Average return for all milk	12·285
Gross return to board	12·285
Expenses of:	
Administration	0·080
Sales promotion	0·090
Co-responsibility levy	0·062
Transport ex-farm } Misc. income charges }	0·590
Average price paid to all producers	11·463

(Table 100, *UK Dairy Facts and Figures*, 1980.)

Each board is required to keep a register of milk producers in its area. This register is available for inspection at the main board offices. In the England and Wales, Scottish and Aberdeen areas a milk producer need register only once with the board even though he may take on the function of wholesale producer, producer–retailer or farmhouse cheesemaker, or any combination of the three. In Northern Ireland and North of Scotland areas a milk producer is required to register with the board in respect of each farm from which he intends to sell milk.

Wholesale Producers
The term 'wholesale producer' is used in England and Wales and in the North of Scotland to describe milk producers who sell milk

direct to the board cn a wholesale contract. This milk is then disposed of through the commercial outlets by the boards. The same arrangement applies in the Scottish, Aberdeen and Northern Ireland areas. Producers are differently described as Ordinary Producers and Milk Licence Holders.

Producer–Retailers

'Producer–retailer' is the term used to describe the producer who retails by authorisation of the Milk Marketing Board part or all of his own milk production direct to consumers. Numbers have declined rapidly during the past twenty years, the decline being accelerated by the growth of the large dairy companies distributing heat-treated (pasteurised or sterilised) milk.

Table 1.2. Milk Producers in England and Wales

Year	Wholesale producers	Producer–retailers
1955	138,305	23,867
1971	74,789	6733
1975	58,532	4756
1979	46,660	3541
1980	42,725	3296

(Table 6. *UK Dairy Facts and Figures, 1980*)

Producer–Processor

This is a new category of producer introduced by the MMB of England and Wales with an amendment to the Milk Marketing Scheme from 1 April 1981.

The new arrangement is for a producer–processor to be allowed to sell his own heat-treated milk in a retail container to someone other than the ultimate consumer, i.e. a shop, supermarket or dairyman.

Any milk withheld from the Board must be under the terms of a specific agreement with the Board and the producer must make payment to the Board for the amount of milk involved.

The payment will be an amount which will leave the producer with the equivalent of the average wholesale producer price plus amounts equal to the average ex-farm haulage cost and bulk addition, and without any deduction for co-responsibility levy. As a processor he will obtain the normal margins.

In this situation there will be no Board requirement for sampling and testing of the supply for compositional quality payment purposes or for the antibiotics deduction scheme.

Farmhouse Cheese

Farmhouse cheesemakers are milk producers who make cheese on the farm under a special contract with the board, who are responsible for the grading of Cheddar, Cheshire and Lancashire 'Farmhouse' cheeses and its sale on behalf of the makers to recognised cheese factors.

The number of farmhouse cheesemakers in England and Wales dropped from a pre-war total of over 1000 to 218 by 1980.

THE EFFECT ON MILK MARKETING BOARDS OF ENTRY INTO THE EEC

When the United Kingdom moved towards entry into the EEC it was likely that the existing legislation of the EEC would threaten the future of the United Kingdom Milk Marketing Boards.

After considerable discussion the EEC Council of Ministers eventually approved two new regulations which would amend Community law in such a way as to ensure that, provided certain conditions were met, the essential powers of the United Kingdom Milk Marketing Boards could be maintained. The two important aspects about the Regulation are that:

● the boards' essential powers remain intact;
● the new arrangements are permanent.

They constitute, therefore, a charter for the board to continue with very little change.

The United Kingdom Government applied for authorisation of the boards under the terms of the new regulations.

The regulations are summarised below.

The First Regulation

This defines the conditions under which an organisation such as the MMB can be authorised, the basic powers which it can be granted and the broad principles under which it must operate. It is applicable in all member countries of the EEC which means that, in theory at least, the Milk Marketing Boards could be set up in other community areas where the prescribed conditions can be fulfilled.

For a Milk Marketing Board or similar organisation to be author-ised it must be shown that:

- it is supported by 80 per cent of producers who vote in a ballot;
- these producers represent at least 50 per cent of milk production in the board's area.

In addition the percentage of milk used direct for human con-sumption as liquid milk or fresh products in the Member State concerned must be at least one and a half times greater than the corresponding percentage for the Community as a whole, while consumption per capita must be greater than the Community average. This means in effect that liquid milk and fresh product consumption must be maintained at more than 38 per cent of production. An earlier proposal was that the level should be at 50 per cent and this would certainly have put the Milk Marketing Board's future at risk if there was a future expansion of United Kingdom manufacture.

Provided these conditions are met, a MMB or similar organi-sation can be granted:

- the exclusive right to purchase all milk from its producers. As before, with this right goes the obligation to buy and market all milk of suitable quality that is offered;
- the right to 'pool' all returns from the market, and to pay equalised prices to its producers, regardless of the use to which the individual producer's milk is put.

The rest of the regulation requires the adoption of rules which will prevent a board from distorting competition, from acting contrary to the Agricultural Policy for milk, or from discriminating unfairly against producers or buyers.

The Second Regulation
This regulation is specific to the United Kingdom and its existing Milk Marketing Boards. It accepts that the United Kingdom can meet the liquid milk consumption requirement and goes on to spell out through a series of articles, specific conditions which must be met if the boards are to be authorised and retained. The more important of the articles refer to:

(a) The *initial referendum* of producers. Each MMB is required to organise a secret ballot to establish whether each voter is in agreement with maintaining the board under the terms of the Regulation. All producers, including producer–retail-ers, will be entitled to vote and each one will have one vote for himself and one for every ten, or part of ten, cows in his possession at a given date. At least 80 per cent of the producers who vote are required to be in favour of the board, but their cows must represent at least half of the total cow numbers in the board's area.

(b) A *subsequent referendum* can be held if at least 1 per cent of producers selling to the board ask for it, but it may not be held less than five years after a previous ballot. Where the required number of votes in favour of the board is not received, the commission is empowered to withdraw the authorisation of that board.

Other articles deal with subjects including the definition of fresh products, the board's commercial operations, producer–retailers and the level of manufacturing prices.

The United Kingdom government will be required to maintain supervision over the marketing boards, as previously, and to modify their rules to bring them into line with the Community Regulations.

From a review of the Regulations it would appear that apart from minor changes the arrangements as a whole would enable the MMB to carry on its work for producers very much as before.

A referendum of producers was held in the autumn of 1978, when there was an overwhelming vote by producers in support of the continuation of the board.

ORGANISATION AND TRENDS IN DAIRY PRODUCTION

The structure of dairy farming has altered considerably during the past twenty-five years.

1. From 1973, the Dairy Herd Conversion Scheme followed by the Non-Marketing of Milk Scheme, together had a significant influence on the decline of milk producers. Between 1975 and 1980 the number of producers declined by 28%.

2. As the number of producers has declined over the years, so the number of dairy cows in the country has actually increased during the same period.

3. The reason why cow numbers have increased over the years despite the decline in registered milk producers is that the average herd size has increased. This has occurred in all the regions of England and Wales, but as Table 1.5 shows, there is a tendency to have larger dairy herds on the eastern and southern parts of the country than in the western areas.

Table 1.3. Registered Milk Producers, England and Wales

	Total producers
1955	142,792
1960	123,137
1965	100,449
1970	80,265
1975	60,279
1976	56,081
1977	53,930
1978	50,065
1979	46,972
1980	43,358

(Table 1. *UK Dairy Facts and Figures*, 1980.)

Table 1.4. Numbers of Dairy Cows—England and Wales

June Census	England and Wales (thousands)
1955	2415
1960	2595
1965	2650
1970	2714
1975	2701
1976	2688
1977	2719
1978	2717
1979	2734
1980 (provisional)	2672

(Table 7, *UK Dairy Facts and Figures*, 1980.)

In the eastern regions, farms are much larger and the dairy units on them are scaled up in size in the hope that they will be economically viable units within the total farm business. In the essentially grass-growing areas of the west the size of the dairy herd is more closely linked to the farm size, there being fewer alternatives to dairying available. However, the farms themselves are traditionally smaller.

The current trends towards increased specialisation and larger herds are likely to accelerate as these are the best ways to combat

Table 1.5. Average Size of Dairy Herds

The Average Numbers of Cows per Herd					
Sample Regions	1960	1965	1970	1975	1978	1979
Northern	19	23	30	42	49	51
West Midland	23	29	37	50	58	62
South Wales	15	18	23	30	36	39
Far Western	16	20	28	37	43	46
Eastern	23	30	37	59	68	72
Southern	28	37	49	70	82	85

(Table 17, *UK Dairy Facts and Figures*, 1980.)

the shrinking of profit margins of the past few years. This shrinkage has resulted from a fairly stable sale price for milk and considerable increases in both the enterprise and fixed costs relating to milk production.

4. There has been a considerable improvement in the average milk yield of the dairy cow during recent years.

Table 1.6. Average Annual Milk Yield per Dairy Cow in England and Wales

Year	Litres
1954–55	3065
1969–70	3755
1974–75	4070
1975–76	4300
1976–77	4350
1977–78	4630
1978–79	4745
1979–80 (provisional)	4810

(Table 20. *UK Dairy Facts and Figures*, 1980)

It would be very difficult to pinpoint the reasons for the increase in yield but in broad terms it must be attributed to the greatly improved management techniques of the previous ten years which in turn were able to exploit and realise the greatly increased genetic potential of the national dairy herd for milk production.

The development of the use of artificial insemination has brought the availability of good quality, proven bulls within the scope of every milk producer in the country and has thus enabled the

Table 1.7. Number of Inseminations by Breeds from MMB Centres in England and Wales

Breed	1979–1980 '000 inseminations	per cent
Dairy		
Ayrshire	18	1·0
Friesians/Holstein	1172	62·3
Guernsey	21	1·1
Jersey	24	1·2
Total	1235	65·5
Dual Purpose		
Dairy Shorthorn	5	0·3
Danish Red/British Dane	—	—
Red Poll	—	—
Welsh Black	5	0·3
Others	1	—
Total	11	0·6
Beef		
Aberdeen Angus	66	3·5
Beef Shorthorn	—	—
Blonde d'Aquitaine	2	0·1
Charolais	126	6·7
Chianina	1	—
Devon	7	0·4
Galloway (inc. Belted)	—	—
Hereford	358	19·1
Highland	—	—
Limousin	34	1·8
Lincoln Red	—	—
Luing	—	—
Maine Anjou	—	—
Murray Grey	18	1·0
Simmental	16	0·9
South Devon	3	0·2
Sussex	4	0·2
Others	1	—
Total	636	33·9
All breeds	1882	100·0

(Table 46. *Dairy Facts and Figures*, MMB, 1980.)

production potential of the national dairy herd to be raised so quickly.

5. From 1955 the breed pattern of the national dairy herd has changed, the proportion of British Friesians increasing from 34·5 per cent to 75 per cent in 1971, and progressing farther along this path. Some indication of the current use of breeds in milk production can best be provided by the number of inseminations by breeds at the insemination centres.

Many of the traditional breeds have lost much ground to newly imported breeds, particularly in the beef section.

The increasing production of beef as a by-product from the national dairy herd has accelerated the trend towards the introduction of the Continental breeds. The shift in the pattern of cattle breeds in general has certainly been due to the economic pressures felt by the dairy industry over the years since the Second World War. (See table 1.7.)

6. A development arising directly from the increases in herd size and yield coupled with an increasing cost of labour, has been the changes in milking systems to be found on many farms.

Table 1.8. Milking Systems—England and Wales

Milking Location and Method	December 1973 Number of systems	December 1978 Number of systems	per cent
Cowshed			
Hand	1985	740	1·5
Bucket	31,172	11,608	23·4
Pipeline	10,714	10,416	21·0
Total (Cowshed)	43,871	22,764	45·9
Parlour			
Abreast	13,571	12,673	25·5
Herringbone	8676	12,617	25·4
Tandem	915 }	} 745	} 1·5
Chute	319 }		
Moveable Bail	1179	431	0·9
Rotary	225	387	0·8
Others	—	—	—
Total (parlour)	24,885	26,853	54·1
Total (both systems)	68,756	49,617	100·0

(Table 21, *UK Dairy Facts and Figures*, 1980.)

The trend has been to more sophistication, so that by December 1978 half the herds in England and Wales were milked through some version of a milking parlour.

During the late seventies there has been a distinct trend towards automation in the milking systems, in an effort to eliminate routine mechanical tests and so leave the herdsman more time to concentrate on husbandry.

MILK QUALITY SCHEMES

In England and Wales certain quality control conditions were agreed by the Joint Committee of the Board and the Dairy Trade Federation as from October 1957. The various aspects of milk quality are dealt with as follows.

The Liaison Chemist Service
This was established in 1957 with the objective of standardising the sampling and testing procedures and equipment throughout the industry and ensuring that all milk producers were treated fairly by the application of such standard procedures.

Hygienic Quality Payment Schemes
The first procedure in the testing of milk occurs on the farm and is an initial inspection by the bulk tank driver. The control scheme allows for the weekly collection of a sample which is subjected to a standard two-hour Resazurin Test for keeping quality. A penalty system is in operation in the event of failures.

Table 1.9. Penalties for failures in milk sampling

Number of failures	Price deduction per litre
First	Nil
Second	0.40p
Third	0.80p
Fourth or subsequent	1.20p

Any producer who persistently supplies milk of poor quality is reported to the Board which may decide to cancel his contract. Similar hygiene schemes operate in the other Board areas of the United Kingdom.

Now that all farm milk supplies are bulk collected, it is generally acknowledged that the standard two-hour Resazurin text is not satisfactory. It does not reflect the standard of hygiene on the farm and is likely to be replaced by a bacterial count method of testing, which will be used in 1982.

A pre-incubated Resazurin test which agrees reasonably well with the bacterial count was introduced in April 1982, to allow milk producers to be better acquainted with the higher standards to be required in the future.

COMPOSITIONAL QUALITY

Payments for milk according to its compositional quality based on total solids content is now in existence throughout the United Kingdom, but in the case of hygienic quality the method of payment varies between different marketing board areas.

England and Wales

Producers are paid on a multi-band scheme for the compositional quality of their milk. Once every month the buyers of milk test each supply of milk for butterfat and solids-not-fat content. The annual average of the total solids, which are calculated every six months, determine the class into which the supply is placed for the next six months commencing May and November each year.

The future production and marketing of milk is thought by the Milk Marketing Board to need to be more closely related to the market return for the different constituents of the milk. An increasingly larger proportion of milk is going to manufacture and this trend is going to affect the future price for milk to the producer.

A new scheme for payment on compositional quality was discussed by the board and representatives of the dairy industry, and was introduced in May 1980. Main features of the new scheme are as follows.

1. Previously, the price a producer received for his milk was determined by adding to, or deducting from, the Basic Price a number of increments according to the average quality of his milk. Under the new scheme there are separate increments of different value for each 0·1 per cent of butterfat and snf (solids-not-fats) instead of a single increment for each 0·1 per cent of total solids as before.

2. The value of the increment for 0·1 per cent of butterfat is higher than that for 0·1 per cent of snf which reflects the weighted average return to the board for these constituents.

3. The basic price is calculated in such a way that all payments to producers above the basic price are balanced by deductions from producers below the basic price.

The basic price for milk is based on the average quality so that over the years from 1973 the basic price was moved from Class 4 (12·00 to 12·09 per cent total solids) to Class 8 (12·40 to 12·49 per cent total solids.)

Milk quality has further improved; the average total solids in 1979 was 12·64 per cent, i.e. within Class 10, although the basic price remained at Class 8.

The new scheme has brought the basic price into line with the average milk quality by raising it to Class 10—reflecting an average

Table 1.10. The Solids-Not-Fat Classification Table From May 1981

Supply with the following latest average snf percentage		Class	Additions (+) or deductions (−) to or from the basic price (pence per litre)		
			Normal	Low-snf	Total
10·20 and less than 10·30		A	+1·320	nil	+1·320
10·10	10·20	B	+1·232	nil	+1·232
10·00	10·10	C	+1·144	nil	+1·144
9·90	10·00	D	+1·056	nil	+1·056
9·80	9·90	E	+0·968	nil	+0·968
9·70	9·80	F	+0·880	nil	+0·880
9·60	9·70	G	+0·792	nil	+0·792
9·50	9·60	H	+0·704	nil	+0·704
9·40	9·50	I	+0·616	nil	+0·616
9·30	9·40	J	+0·528	nil	+0·528
9·20	9·30	K	+0·440	nil	+0·440
9·10	9·20	L	+0·352	nil	+0·352
9·00	9·10	M	+0·264	nil	+0·264
8·90	9·00	N	+0·176	nil	+0·176
8·80	8·90	O	+0·088	nil	+0·088
8·70	8·80	P	nil	nil	nil
8·60	8·70	Q	−0·088	nil	−0·088
8·50	8·60	R	−0·176	nil	−0·176
8·40	8·50	S	−0·264	−0·200	−0·464
8·30	8·40	T	−0·352	−0·500	−0·852
8·20	8·30	U	−0·440	−0·600	−1·040
8·10	8·20	V	−0·528	−0·700	−1·228
8·00	8·10	W	−0·616	−0·800	−1·416
Less than 8·00		X	−0·704	−0·900	−1·604
Unclassified		Y	As published in "Milk Producer"		
Unclassified, Islands	Channel	Z	,, ,,		

(*The Milk Quality Testing Schemes*, MMB May 1981.)

Table 1.11. The Butterfat Classification Table From May 1981

Supply with the following latest average butterfat percentage		Class	Additions (+) or deductions (−) to or from the basic price (pence per litre)
For each 0·1 per cent above 5·00 per cent		27 and Higher	+0·125
4·90 and less than 5·00		26	+1·584
4·80	4·90	25	+1·440
4·70	4·80	24	+1·296
4·60	4·70	23	+1·152
4·50	4·60	22	+1·008
4·40	4·50	21	+0·864
4·30	4·40	20	+0·720
4·20	4·30	19	+0·576
4·10	4·20	18	+0·432
4·00	4·10	17	+0·288
3·90	4·00	16	+0·144
3·80	3·90	15	nil
3·70	3·80	14	−0·144
3·60	3·70	13	−0·288
3·50	3·60	12	−0·432
3·40	3·50	11	−0·576
3·30	3·40	10	−0·720
3·20	3·30	9	−0·864
3·10	3·20	8	−1·008
3·00	3·10	7	−1·152
2·90	3·00	6	−1·296
2·80	2·90	5	−1·440
2·70	2·80	4	−1·584
2·60	2·70	3	−1·728
2·50	2·60	2	−1·872
Less than 2·50		1	−2·016
Unclassified		UN	As published monthly in "Milk Producer"
,, Channel Islands		UC	,, ,, ,,

(*The Milk Quality Testing Schemes*, MMB May 1981.)

butterfat level (3·91 per cent) and an average snf level (8·73 per cent) which together give a total solids of 12·64.

4. The new scheme takes in all supplies including Channel Island, who are paid an additional flat-rate premium throughout the year.

5. A producer will gain or lose under the new scheme according to the ratio of butterfat to snf in his supply. He will receive one and two-third times as much for butterfat as for snf.

This emphasis on butterfat is likely to influence farmers in their bull selection when planning future herd-breeding policy. However, income from milk will still be directly related to the total weight of constituents produced, i.e. a combination of quantity and quality of milk. Returns may be improved by either greater production or improving the quality; resources on every farm must be blended to give the maximum possible return.

Scotland—Scottish Milk Marketing Board

Arrangements for the Scottish MMB's scheme are that producers' wholesale supply is sampled by the buyer four times each month

Table 1.12. Scotland—Payments

	Addition to or deduction from, Pool Price (pence per litre)	
Total solids (per cent)	From 1st October 1978	From 1st April 1980
13·20 and over	+0·48	+0·60
13·00–13·19	+0·40	+0·50
12·80–12·99	+0·32	+0·40
12·60–12·79	+0·24	+0·30
12·40–12·59	+0·16	+0·20
12·20–12·39	+0·08	+0·10
12·00–12·19	**Pool Price**	**Pool Price**
11·80–11·99	−0·15	−0·20
11·50–11·79	−0·25	−0·30
11·49 and under	−0·80	−1·00

(*UK Dairy Facts and Figures* 1980.)

and samples are sent to the central laboratory for the testing of
total solids content. Payment of premium or deduction each month
is made on the simple average of the four tests for the month.

Aberdeen Milk Marketing Board
Tests of wholesale producers' supplies are made weekly at the
board's central laboratory. Premiums and penalties are applied on
the basis of the simple average of the monthy test results.
    The scale of penalties or premiums are as shown in Table 1.13.

Table 1.13. Aberdeen—Payments

Total solids (per cent)	Addition to, or deduction from, Pool Price (pence per litre) from 1 April 1977
13·40 and over	+0·130
13·29–13·39	+0·110
13·00–13·19	+0·090
12·80–12·99	+0·070
12·60–12·79	+0·040
12·40–12·59	+0·020
12·20–12·39	**Pool Price**
12·00–12·19	−0·165
11·50–11·99	−0·440
11·49 and under	−0·770

(*UK Dairy Facts and Figures*, 1980.)

North of Scotland
Wholesale producers' supplies are tested monthly by buyers of
milk and by the board. The tests determine total solids, butterfat
and snf content.
    From January 1973, the result of the current month's test for
butterfat when added to the sum of the results for the previous
eleven months has formed the basis of the quality payment adjustment to the producers' price.
    From 1 July 1980, price adjustments to wholesale producers
supplies will be as shown in Table 1.14.

Table 1.14. North of Scotland—Payments

Moving annual total butterfat % with 102% or more snf	Band number	Addition to, or deduction from, Pool Price (pence per litre) from 1 July 1980
50·40 and above	8	+0·39
49·20 to 50·399	7	+0·26
48·00 to 49·199	6	+0·13
46·80 to 47·999	**5**	**Pool Price**
45·60 to 46·799	4	−0·13
44·40 to 45·599	3	−0·26
43·20 to 44·399	2	−0·39
Below 43·20	1	−0·52

A penalty of 0·20p per litre is applied to a supply with an annual total solids not-fat below 102%.

Northern Ireland

The scheme in Northern Ireland is based on the testing of wholesale producers' supplies once a week and combines two weeks' samples for testing of the butterfat and snf content. The average total solids of the supply for the month is determined from these twice-monthy tests.

Table 1.15. Northern Ireland—Payments

Total solids % with 8·40% or more snf (per cent)	Addition to, or deduction from, base price (pence per litre) from 1 April		Total solids % with 8·40% or more snf (per cent)	Addition to, or deduction from, base price (pence per litre) from 1 April	
	1977	1980		1977	1980
15·00 and above	+1·82	+2·34	13·00–13·09	+0·42	+0·54
14·90–14·99	+1·75	+2·25	12·90–12·99	+0·35	+0·45
14·80–14·89	+1·68	+2·16	12·80–12·89	+0·28	+0·36
14·70–14·79	+1·61	+2·07	12·70–12·79	+0·21	+0·27
14·60–14·69	+1·54	+1·98	12·60–12·69	+0·14	+0·18
14·50–14·59	+1·47	+1·89	12·50–12·59	+0·07	+0·09
14·40–14·49	+1·40	+1·80	**12·40–12·49**	**Base Price**	**Base Price**

Table 1.15—*cont.*

Total solids % with 8·40% or more snf (per cent)	Addition to, or deduction from, base price (pence per litre) from 1 April		Total solids % with 8·40% or more snf (per cent)	Addition to, or deduction from, base price (pence per litre) from 1 April	
	1977	1980		1977	1980
14·30–14·39	+1·33	+1·71	12·30–12·39	−0·07	−0·09
14·20–14·29	+1·26	+1·62	12·20–12·29	−0·14	−0·18
14·10–14·19	+1·19	+1·53	12·10–12·19	−0·21	−0·27
14·00–14·09	+1·12	+1·44	12·00–12·09	−0·28	−0·36
13·90–13·99	+1·05	+1·35	11·90–11·99	−0·35	−0·45
13·80–13·89	+0·98	+1·26	11·80–11·89	−0·42	−0·54
13·70–13·79	+0·91	+1·17	11·70–11·79	−0·49	−0·63
13·60–13·69	+0·84	+1·08	11·60–11·69	−0·56	−0·72
13·50–13·59	+0·77	+0·99	11·50–11·59	−0·70	−0·90
13·40–13·49	+0·70	+0·90	11·40–11·49	−0·84	−1·08
13·30–13·39	+0·63	+0·81	11·20–11·39	−0·98	−1·26
13·20–13·29	+0·56	+0·72	11·00–11·19	−0·12	−1·44
13·10–13·19	+0·49	+0·63	Below 11·00	−1·26	−1·62

(*UK Dairy Facts and Figures*, 1980.)

Changes in Payment on Compositional Quality

There has been quite a significant change in the payment policy of the England and Wales boards, as from May 1981, and it is possible that there will be future modifications to the existing schemes of the other four United Kingdom boards.

The Antibiotic Testing Scheme

A test for antibiotics and other inhibitory substances is applied to each ex-farm supply at least once a month. A first test failure incurs a deduction of 5·00 pence per litre applied to the whole consignment which fails. A second failure incurs a deduction of 7·00 pence per litre. At this stage the supply is placed on a special Testing List for more frequent testing with each subsequent failure incurring a deduction of 9·00 pence per litre.

Sediment Testing Scheme

A voluntary sediment testing scheme was introduced in March 1974. A test result indicating contamination of 2 mg or more per litre was considered unsatisfactory and resulted in a test failure. Milk was rejected in cases of consistent contamination.

A mandatory Sediment Testing Scheme is likely to be introduced in October 1981 on a monthly basis. A contamination of 3 mg or more of a standard sediment per litre will be regarded as a test failure.

Brucellosis Testing Scheme
Every herd is tested monthly for brucellosis by use of the Milk Ring Test.

The intention is to ensure that accredited herds remain free from brucellosis infection. Positive test results are notified to the Ministry of Agriculture who then make further investigations.

Mastitis Cell Count
The sample of milk used for Brucellosis testing is also used for monitoring the herd mastitis cell count. The result is entered on to the producer's payment advice together with the rolling 12 month average.

Milk Collection and Sampling

All ex-farm milk supplies are now bulk collected in England and Wales. Previously, in the days of churn collection, a milk lorry driver would check that each churn contained milk of a satisfactory nature. Now, with the bulk tank system in operation, a greatly increased responsibility rests on the tanker drivers to ensure that (i) sub-standard milk which might contaminate a whole tanker load is not bulked with other supplies; (ii) a representative sample is obtained for testing; and (iii) the producers' supplies are correctly recorded.

The main features which are looked for in the initial inspection of the bulk tank supply before collection are:

(a) The milk must not have bad or sour smells, and no blood or foreign matter on the surface.
(b) There must be no smells, foreign matter or blood evident after the milk has been agitated in the tank for at least two minutes.
(c) The milk temperature must be at 45°F (7°C) or below.

If a consignment does not meet with these requirements, it is possible that the tanker driver can consult with his depot and this can lead to the consignment being rejected for collection.

Central Testing Laboratories
The MMB in England and Wales have decided to introduce Central Testing by mid 1982.

Six new laboratories are planned for the purpose of testing all milk supplies instead of testing being carried out by 250 Creamery and Dairy laboratories as at present.

The new system should provide far greater uniformity in testing, quicker introduction of new techniques, and overall a more comprehensive monitoring of milk supplies than is at present possible.

CHAPTER 2

REGULATIONS GOVERNING
MILK PRODUCTION

FROM the point of view of the consumer, milk 'quality' signifies the three main characteristics of milk which determine its suitability for human consumption:

● its cleanliness and keeping quality
● its freedom from pathogenic infection
● its nutritional value based on its content of fat and other milk solids.

THE RULES SUMMARISED

Legislation as it affects milk production has been framed to cover these three aspects, and what follows is a summarised account of the form in which statutory recognition has been given to these aims.

Before milk can be sold as liquid milk for human consumption, the producer must be registered with the Ministry of Agriculture and conditions of production on the farm must comply with the provisions of the latest Milk and Dairies (General Regulations) 1959.

Clean Buildings

Inspections of conditions of production on the farm are made by the county dairy husbandry adviser. The provisions regarding dairy premises lay down that ventilation and lighting of all dairy buildings must be adequate, with a clean approach and a suitable water supply.

Internal walls and floors liable to soiling by dung or urine must be of impervious material, and floors and gutters must be sloped to convey urine to a trapped drain outside the building. The alternative of providing absorbent material for the urine is, however, permitted.

Milking bails are able to conform to these regulations if moved sufficiently frequently to avoid contamination, or if sited on a concrete platform.

Dung must be removed at least once daily from cowsheds and milking parlours and the approaches to either must be kept clean. Milking must be carried out in good light, after cleaning the flanks and udders of the cows, and withdrawing the foremilk of each cow into a separate vessel and then discarding it.

Milk Storage

The milk should be cooled in refrigerated bulk tanks to a temperature of 4·5°C and held at this level until collection. Milk must not be handled or processed (e.g. bottled) in any place liable to contamination. So the milkroom or dairy must not, in general, have direct access to the cowshed, fuel or food store, nor can it be used for any other purpose except the storage of milk utensils.

Before milking all the equipment must be thoroughly cleansed and sterilised.

Powers are given to veterinary officers of the Ministry of Agriculture to inspect the cattle on the farm, and to authorised persons to take samples of milk or inspect the premises to see that they comply with the regulations.

The milk producer must not use any milk either for liquid or manufacture from a cow suffering from a notifiable disease, e.g. TB, anthrax or foot-and-mouth disease or any cow suffering from acute mastitis or any udder infection likely to convey disease.

Furthermore, the producer is obliged to notify the local Medical Officer of Health of any outbreak of a notifiable disease—typhoid fever, scarlet fever, undulant fever or dysentery—in his own household or the household of any of his employees, and to grant facilities for investigation and control of the manner in which the milk is to be handled before sale when such circumstances exist.

Specially Designated Milk

Nearly all milk sold by retail in Great Britain must be specially designated milk.

In England and Wales the special designations are 'untreated'; 'pasteurised'; 'sterilised'; and 'ultra heat treated'.

Untreated is used in respect of raw milk, i.e. milk which has not been heat-treated and which has been bottled or cartoned on the farm or at the dairy. These milks must pass certain tests, and licences to use the designations are controlled by current regulation, The Milk (Special Designations) Regulation 1963 Amendments—1979. The Regulation is to be changed to comply with EEC requirements. In Scotland the special designations are 'premium' and 'standard' in respect of raw milk, and 'pasteurised', 'sterilised' and 'ultra heat treated' for the heat-treated milks. From 1982, all farm bottled non-pasteurised milk will continue to have a green cap and also must bear the description of raw unpasteurised milk.

Compositional Standards for Liquid Milk

Prior to entry to the EEC, the presumptive legal minimum standards were 3·0 per cent butterfat and 8·5 per cent solids-not-fat, applicable to all milk offered for sale by producers or dairies.

Under EEC regulations, Member States were required to adopt within their territories from 1 October, 1976 either of two heat-treated whole milks for sale to customers—standardised or non-standardised. The United Kingdom has elected to market non-standardised whole milk to the consumer of liquid milk for which the Regulation prescribes a minimum butterfat of 3·0 per cent but no minimum for solids-not-fat. The Regulation also permits the sale of untreated (raw) milk at its natural fat content and at any higher fat content the Member State may determine. The existing requirement of a minimum fat content of 4·0 per cent for Channel Islands, Jersey, Guernsey or South Devon, whether heat-treated or untreated, is therefore permissible under EEC regulations.

Since the Regulation leaves Member States free to determine the compositional standards for raw milk, the existing United Kingdom requirement of a minimum solids-not-fat content of 8·5 per cent for premium milk continues. Milk on retail sale in Great Britain is subject to testing for cleanliness, adulteration, composition etc., by the Agricultural Departments or the food and drug authorities.

Pasteurisation

The milk may be pasteurised by either of two methods:

(a) **Holder Process.** Milk heated to 63–5°C and held within that temperature range for at least thirty minutes and then immediately cooled to a temperature not exceeding 10°C.

(b) **High Temperature Short-Time Process.** Milk heated to 72°C and retained at that temperature for not less than fifteen seconds and then immediately cooled to not more than 10°C.

Provision is made for any new method of pasteurisation to be adopted, provided the approval of the Minister is obtained.

Sterilisation

The milk is filtered, homogenised and heated to a temperature not less than 100°C in sealed bottles and held at the temperature for sufficient time to comply with the turbidity test applied to sterilised milk, details of which are given in the third schedule of the regulations.

Ultra-Heat Treatment

This involves heating the milk to really high temperatures—135–149°C—for a few seconds and then rapidly cooling it. Heating is by indirect means (e.g. heat exchangers) rather than by injection of steam, as in the Continental process.

UHT milk can be bottled or cartoned and will keep for long periods. The sale of ultra heat-treated milk was made legal after 1 October 1965 and, because of its long-keeping qualities, could change the pattern of milk retailing for liquid consumption.

METHODS THAT MATTER

The basis of a satisfactory milk supply is laid on the farm. Good facilities in the way of buildings and equipment make the task of clean milk production easier, but by no means guarantee clean milk if the methods used are careless or slovenly. If clean milk is to be produced, attention must be particularly paid to **avoiding the contamination of the milk during milking.**

When the milk leaves the udder its bacterial population is low, 200–300 bacteria per millilitre, and these organisms are, if the udder is healthy, quite harmless to the consumer.

During milking, however, contamination can arise from a dust-laden atmosphere, from unclean udders or teats, dirty hands of the milker, or lastly—and this is a most important source— contact with unsterile utensils. Too much emphasis cannot be given to this fact. All dairy utensils must be first of all made physically clean and then sterilised properly either by steam or chemical means to ensure that they are bacteriologically clean.

In clean milk production a definite routine should be decided upon and adhered to; the simpler that routine can be the more likely is it to be effective. It is suggested that the following routine measures represent minimum requirements in that respect.

- Cows should be kept as clean as possible by suitable housing and adequate litter. Cubicle housing assists in keeping cows clean.
- Udders and teats should be washed in warm water (49°C) not sooner than three minutes before milking can be commenced. Use paper towels with spray hoses.
- Where mastitis is prevalent a hypochlorite should be added to the washing water. Wipe off any surplus moisture before taking the foremilk by use of the strip cup—a job that should be done immediately before milking begins.

Washing Procedures
Immediately after milking, the equipment should be rinsed with water and then sterilised using the Acid Boiling Water System, or by the Circulation Cleaning System.

For the former it is essential that the temperature of the hot water leaving the plant is at a temperature of not less than 90°C.

For the latter system, the solution in the wash trough should be maintained at a temperature of at least 60°C. Full details on cleaning procedures are available in the appropriate Ministry leaflets.

The cleaning of bulk tanks can be done by use of approved detergents and sterilising agents, using a manual or automatic cold cleaning system. The technique involves rinsing with cold water, leaving the sterilising agent on for twenty minutes, and finally rinsing off with cold water.

Dairy Farms are Food Factories

Great progress has been made in the re-equipment of dairy buildings for greater cleanliness in milk production, but undoubtedly the greatest single factor is scrupulous cleanliness of milking utensils, and this is as much a matter of method as of means.

The modern dairy farm is a food factory where standards of cleanliness must be of a high order to encourage the confidence of the consumer in its product and to ensure that milk reaches the consumer with keeping qualities above criticism.

Even the subsequent heat treatment of milk (e.g. pasteurisation) does not remove the obligation on the producer to market a product of high hygienic standards.

The legal minimum standards for milk sold in England and Wales are 3·0 per cent butterfat and 8·5 per cent solids-not-fat; in Scotland the butterfat minimum is 3·5 per cent.

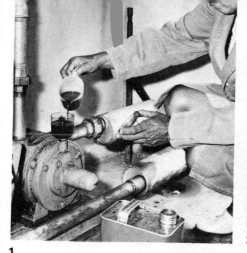

1

2

MILKING MACHINE MAINTENANCE
The Vacuum Pump

1 Air extraction capacity of lubricated vacuum pumps can be seriously impaired if oil level is allowed to fall. Check level daily and top up as necessary. Use type of oil recommended by pump manufacturer.

2 After being in use for a while V-belts tend to stretch, become slack and slip off pulleys. Check daily to ensure that there is no more than 13 mm 'play' at mid-point between pump and drive motor. Also check for signs of belt wear.

4 Constant tension and vibration can cause some lateral movement of motor on its mountings, leading to misalignment of pulleys. If not remedied, it can cause rapid belt wear and loss of pump efficiency. Check by putting a straight edge along pulleys, as shown; it should touch all four edges of pulleys if alignment is correct.

3 If belts are slack but in good condition, tension them by moving position of motor in relation to pump. If belts are worn, replace them and ensure a matched pair is fitted. Note facilities for lateral adjustment of motor (arrowed).

3

4

7

5

6

8

9

5 Air extraction rate of pump depends on its speed of rotation; any fall-off in rpm will result in reduction in cfm of air extracted. If a low vacuum level is noted (despite correct oil level and belt tension), pump may not be running at its correct speed. Check this with a tachometer held against pully rim or, preferably, pump shaft. Alteration of pump speed is a task for a qualified maintenance engineer.

6 Once every 6 months wash interior of pump, to flush away dirt and carbon deposits; these could cause a vane to stick in its slot and thus impair efficiency. Remove oil reservoir and pour in a litre of paraffin or diesel fuel.

7 Rock belts to and fro a few times, to work paraffin around inside. After removing silencer, start up and run pump for half a minute or so, to eject paraffin and dirt through exhaust. Then pour in eggcupful of pump oil, refit silencer, replace and refill oil reservoir.

8 Every 6 months lubricate shaft bearings of electric drive motor, according to manufacturs' instructions. Photo shows bearing nipples being given a shot of high-melting point grease from a gun. On some types of motor a small cap is filled with grease and screwed down onto lubricating point.

9 If milking plant has a stand-by motor for emergency use, it should be turned over and started once a week. This not only ensures that it will start readily when needed, but also maintains a film of oil on interior surfaces and working parts, to prevent rust.

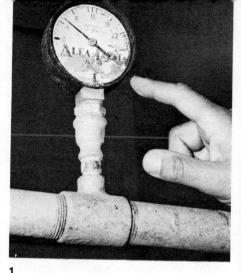

1

1 Check that gauge registers recommended vacuum level when pump is operating and returns to zero when pump is switched off. Pictured is a gauge with a broken glass which has seized up as a result of corrosion.

2

MILKING MACHINE MAINTENANCE

The Vacuum System

2 Check that there is an adequate vacuum reserve by opening tap and allowing pointer on gauge to drop back to 150–175 mm of mercury. Then close tap, and using the second hand of watch, note time taken for vacuum to rise from 250 mm to 380 mm or 200 mm to 330 mm. Recovery time should not exceed 3 seconds.

3 Listen to vacuum controller when pump is operating and correct vacuum level is shown on gauge. Hiss of air being admitted at steady intake rate, without fluttering, confirms an adequate vacuum reserve and indicates that controller is working efficiently.

4 If previous tests show a lack of vacuum reserve, check whole system for air leaks (which are often audible). Start by inspecting rim of sanitary trap bucket for dents, and examine lid gasket for signs of wear. Renew gasket if necessary and clean at monthly intervals.

3

4

5

5 Inspect sanitary trap after each milking to check that it is clean and dry. If it contains milk, wash out vacuum pipe immediately and investigate how milk entered vacuum system (a split liner, for example). Otherwise, washing is a monthly routine task.

6

6 Wash out vacuum pump by attaching hose to tap furthest from pump, draw a solution of non-foaming detergent through pipeline. Take care not to flood pump. Lift hose in and out of solution to create a surging effect in pipe. Flush detergent out of system with hot clean water. Empty sanitary bucket after each operation and finish by drawing air through pipe for a few minutes to dry out.

7 After washing out, use a spirit level to check that system is properly aligned. Each section of the vacuum pipe should slope down to a drainage point (arrowed) or to sanitary trap. Any sagging or distortion of line should be corrected.

8 When vacuum line has been cleared, check for slack joints and badly fitting taps. Also look for cracks in rubber joints (arrowed) in the milk line. Dismantle washing and drainage taps once a year for cleaning and inspection.

7

8

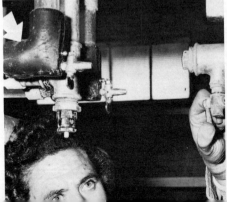

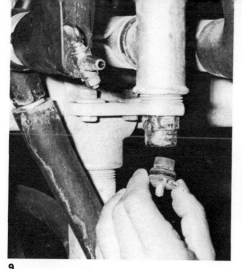

9

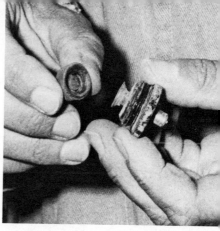

10

9 Some vacuum lines are fitted with automatic drain valves at lowest point of each section. A flake of rust or deposit of dirt inside can cause valve to stick in partly open position and allow entry of air. After washing vacuum pipe it is a good opportunity to remove each valve . . .

10 . . . for examination and cleaning. Check that plunger moves freely in its seating and renew rubber gasket if it is worn or distorted. Clean thread of pipeline before screwing in valve, and listen to ensure there is no audible air leakage when it is back in place.

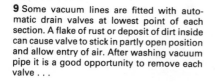

11 Test stall taps for leaks and free movement after vacuum pipeline wash. At 6-monthly intervals dismantle each tap for thorough inspection; wipe valve and its seating clean and brush out nozzle.

12 Dust and moisture drawn in by vacuum controller can build up to form a grinding paste and damage moving parts. Once a week, therefore, strip down controller and clean valve and seating with cotton-wool soaked in methylated spirts.

11

12

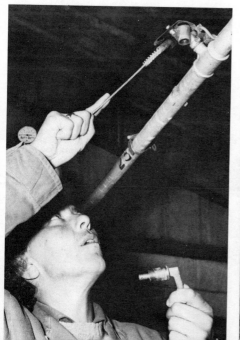

13

13 Check for a worn valve which can cause a leak and a drop in vacuum. Clean and inspect rubber gasket and renew if it shows signs of wear or distortion. See that all internal parts are completely dry before re-assembly.

14 Use stiff brush to clean wire gauze that protects air inlet. Take great care when handling components of vacuum controller, since even slightest damage can seriously affect its efficiency.

15 Dead weight types of vacuum controller must be level to work properly. If unit has a flat top (as this model) place a spirit level on it and ensure it is horizontal. Then rotate spirit level through 90° and repeat check.

16 If weight-operated controller is suspended (as this one) ensure that it is rigidly installed and make a two-dimensional check that it is in a true vertical position. Spring-operated controllers (not illustrated) should have their spring tension tested.

15

16

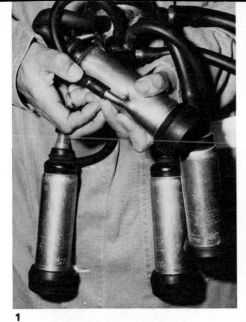

1

MILKING MACHINE MAINTENANCE

The Pulsation System

1 Check rubber for pinholes and cracks, particularly at ends of pulse tubes where they fit onto metal connections. Renew at first signs of wear. Leaks in tubes distort pulsation and impair efficiency.

2 A split liner can leak milk and wash solution into cavity between itself and teat cup shell, and thence into short and long pulse tubes. When this happens, clean out tubes by flushing with hot detergent solution. Special rods fitted with brush heads should be used to shift any build-up of milk solids in tubes.

3 Slugs of milk and water can get into tubes which connect relays and which must be kept clean and dry if a proper pulse is to be maintained at teat cups. Disconnect and blow

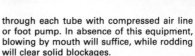

2

through each tube with compressed air line or foot pump. In absence of this equipment, blowing by mouth will suffice, while rodding will clear solid blockages.

4 An abnormal pulse rate can stem from dust being drawn into pulsators and relays, forming blockages and restricting admission of air needed to inflate teat-cut liners. Clean air inlet ports of dust deposits at each weekly inspection.

4

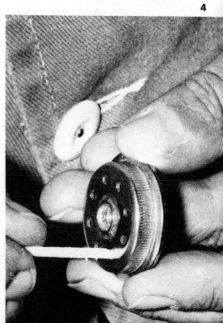

3

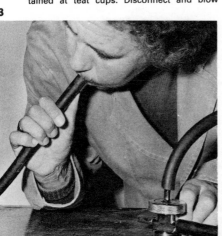

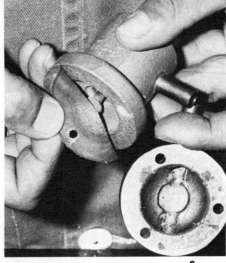

5

6

5 Air inlet of pulsator is usually fitted with a filter made of fine wire gauze. With air being drawn through, filter becomes coated with dust and should be cleaned with a stiff brush.

6 Each pulsator and relay has a rubber diaphragm which regulates passage of air to teat cups; this should be kept clean and dry. Renew every year or sooner if it shows any sign of distortion.

7 As it is important not to interchange parts, dismantle and clean pulsators and relays one at a time, using a cloth dipped in methylated spirits.

8 After cleaning, check pulsation rate by blocking three teat cups (either by plugging or by inverting clawpiece) and inserting a thumb in fourth. When unit is operating, use a watch and count the number of times liner collapses in 60 seconds. Compare with manufacturers' specifications (usually 50 and 60 pulsations per minute).

9 If pulsation speed is too fast or too slow, it must be corrected. Adjust pulse rate by turning simple regulator fitted to some types of pulsator. With others, precalibrated at factory, consult qualified dairy maintenance engineer.

7

8

9

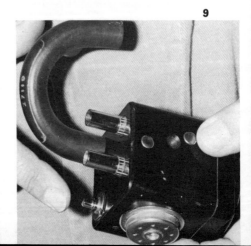

MILKING MACHINE MAINTENANCE

Milking Units and Pipeline

1 Examine teat cup liners regularly for splits, which allow milk leakage and lead to blockages in the pulse tubes. Distortion of mouthpiece or barrel of liners should also be looked for as it impairs milking efficiency. Replace worn liners immediately. **1**

2 Air should only enter through clawpiece air bleed: any which is admitted elsewhere impairs milking efficiency. So check long and short milk tubes frequently for leaks in form of pinholes and cracks (which occur particularly at the ends of tubes where they fit on to metal connections). **2**

3 Once a week, check rubber connecting sleeves and elbow joints of milkline for poor fit, leaks, cracks (as shown) or signs of perishing. Replace if necessary and renew annually as routine maintenance. (Note: if pipeline is jointed correctly, sleeves should only be disturbed if in need of replacement.) **3**

4

5

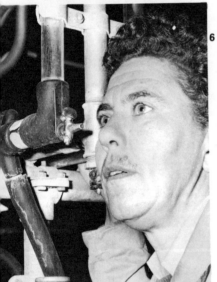

6

4 Examine points where long milk tubes are connected to milkline. With constant use, metal connectors tend to get bent and rubber gaskets wear thin. Check that connectors fit well and replace worn gaskets. (Note: air leaks are often plainly audible if inspection is carried out while the plant is operating.)

5 Check alignment of milkline with a spirit level. Each section of pipeline should slope down towards a drainage point. Adjust any sags to prevent water lying in pipeline after cleaning.

6 Listen for tell-tale hiss or air leaks in the milkline drain taps while plant is operating. If a valve is found to be loose in its seating it should be tightened, if it is of an adjustable type, or whole tap should be replaced.

7 By-passed by circulation cleaning, milk residues tend to collect inside drain taps and the trickle of water which is let out after cleaning has insufficient pressure to shift them. So milkline drain taps should be dismantled once a month for inspection and cleaning.

7

Milk falling below these minimum standards is presumed to have been adulterated and the onus of proof to the contrary rests on the milk producer.

Public health authorities are empowered to take milk samples at any stage in production or distribution and can institute legal proceedings against the producers of any milk which does not conform to the required minimum standards.

Producers involved in such proceedings have the right of 'appeal to the cow'—the taking of samples on the farm at milking time—and, should these prove to be below compositional standards, the appeal is allowed.

But an exacting test, known as the 'freezing point test', is now usually applied and it can determine—to within very close limits—whether water has been added.

Approximate freezing point of milk is −0·545°C. It varies from breed to breed, cow to cow, and to allow for maximum variation, milk with a freezing point of −0·53°C is suspected of being adulterated with water. Although usually accepted in a Court of Law, the standard is not statutory.

CHAPTER 3

BUILDINGS AND EQUIPMENT FOR DAIRY FARMING

FOR milk production to be carried out on farms, certain items of equipment are essential.

These can be classified into three categories:

- Accommodation for the cow—and young stocking, if rearing is undertaken;
- equipment for milking the cow and subsequent handling of the milk;
- fixed equipment in respect of fences, roads and water supplies, and means of conserving dung and liquid manure.

THE QUESTION OF OUT-WINTERING

The extent and nature of the buildings on a dairy farm for stock accommodation are determined largely by whether or not cattle are to be housed indoors during the winter. Out-wintering requires well-drained, sheltered land which not only resists winter poaching but is also capable of recovering quickly in the spring. Consequently, out-wintering of dairy cows is almost exclusively found on the free-draining chalk, limestone or sandy soil of sheltered areas of southern England. Even in these areas very few herds are now out-wintered; it is generally realised that the extra feed required to keep the herd in good physical condition and to produce milk is of such a high level that the profitability of the exercise would be in doubt. Providing buildings requires considerable capital but on the other hand it is very important for the well-being of both the dairy herd and the staff looking after the herd.

Obviously the economic aspects are all-important and consideration has to be given to the cost of providing stock accommodation. During the seventies the trend has been to provide buildings designed to be put up at a less capital cost than the traditional brick and stone types but with a much reduced life expectancy.

In nearly all cases stock is required to be housed through the winter, particularly during such extreme conditions as in the winter of 1978–9 and 1981–2.

Young stock certainly need winter accommodation. More mature stock, incalf heifers, dry cows etc., can be left outside but only in extreme circumstances. Quite apart from cow nutrition, it is also obviously an advantage for the utilisation of labour when cattle are housed in some kind of a group.

GENERAL BUILDING LAYOUT

During the course of a winter, a cow is likely to consume something between four and ten tonne of food and to produce four to six tonne of dung, according to the intake of the animal, the productive level attained and the dry-matter content of the diet. Such large amounts of food and waste products do present a large problem and really should be considered a major factor in the planning of any new layout. There have become available over the years many ways in which food and waste products can be handled mechanically; the problem, however, is to combine the efficiency of handling with an economic cost of providing the various mechanical aids. Basic standards for cow housing are laid down under the Milk and Dairies Regulations, 1959.

The main features which should govern the construction of any cow housing are as follows:

1. The cows must be housed in comfort with adequate light and ventilation. A good supply of water is essential, up to 40–50 litres per day would be necessary for a high-yielding cow. The dry-matter content of the ration would markedly affect the water intake.

2. Cow housing should be planned to bring together housing, feeding and milking operations so that dairy staff can use their time more effectively. Modern large-span buildings do enable all the functions to be carried out under one roof.

3. A site for dairy buildings should be situated on a well-drained and preferably elevated site, and the availability of service roads, water and electricity should be considered. If possible, the situation should also be in the centre of the grazing area. Walking long distances uses up energy which should be used in the production of milk.

4. Attention must be given to the siting of the food stores, silage

clamps, etc. The ideal would be for the food to be stored under the same umbrella-type building. Unfortunately the cost of such a policy is likely to be exorbitant. In all cases a balance between practicability and profit must be looked for.

5. Where possible, additional accommodation in the form of isolation boxes, calf pens and bull housing should be provided on the same site.

Current trends are towards the organisation of heifer rearing and this implies stricter control over feeding and management. Proximity to the dairy herd allows more effective management practices to be applied.

6. The dairy must be next to the milking parlour, and large enough to hold the bulk tanks necessary for the daily production.

The size of the bulk tank must be given considerable thought. Factors which will determine the size required include size of herd, calving pattern (all the year round or block calving) and the system of management which will be designed to produce a lower or higher yield per cow. Bulk tanks are expensive and once installed should be capable of coping with the herd production for several subsequent years.

Where tanks are to be replaced, forward budgets would need to take account of whether money needs to be borrowed and if so, how much.

A Revolution in Cow Housing

Traditionally, cows were housed in cowsheds and tied by the neck, using chains, leather straps or metal yokes. After the Second World War the increase in labour costs provoked a move from cowsheds and this was started by the introduction of the loose housing system on straw. During the sixties, the yard and parlour system was widely installed. Bucket milking and the more recently introduced pipeline milking were increasingly replaced by the modern milking parlour.

The Yard-and-Parlour System
The new system gave a greater flexibility of cow numbers linked to the increase in herd size and the need for speeding up the milking process.

One disadvantage of loose housing associated with increasing cow numbers was the loss of the opportunity for individual attention to cows. This feature was to some extent minimised by the feeding

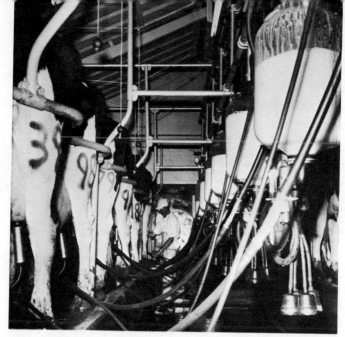

During the last fifteen years there has been a marked trend towards the herringbone milking parlour. Note ease of identification and recording facility.

A vacuum recorder being used to test the action of the pulsators.

These cows, on self-fed silage, are housed in winter in this cow kennel house built of wood and corrugated sheets.

Udder washing with hand spray; note rubber gloves:

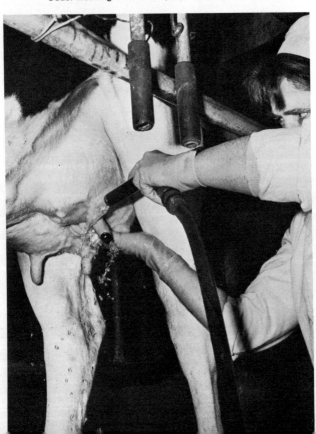

This cubicle building contains 190 stalls of tubular metal construction. Partly open sides provide good ventilation and prevent roof condensation.

A simple type of cubicle installed in a shed with a wide slatted-floor passageway.

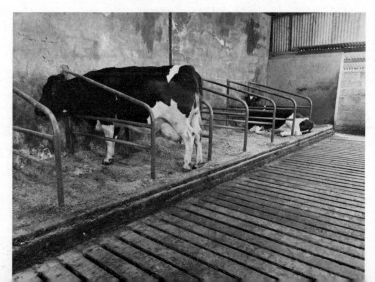

SEVEN WAYS WITH CUBICLES

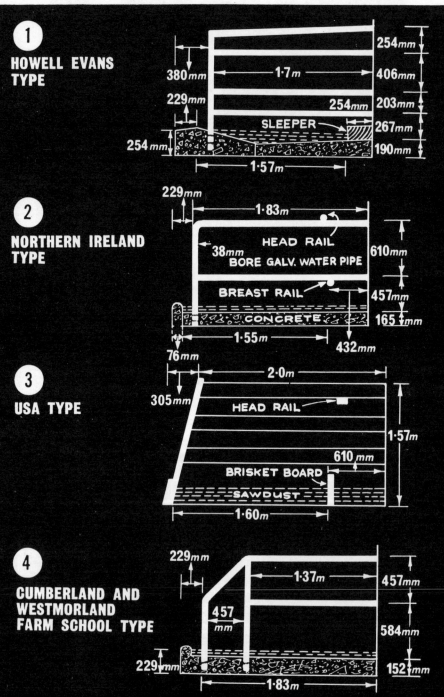

1 HOWELL EVANS TYPE

254mm
380mm 1·7m 406mm
229mm 254mm 203mm
SLEEPER 267mm
254mm 190mm
1·57m

2 NORTHERN IRELAND TYPE

229mm
1·83m
38mm HEAD RAIL 610mm
BORE GALV. WATER PIPE
BREAST RAIL 457mm
CONCRETE 165 mm
1·55m
432mm

3 USA TYPE

76mm
2·0m
305mm HEAD RAIL
1·57m
610 mm
BRISKET BOARD
SAWDUST
1·60m

4 CUMBERLAND AND WESTMORLAND FARM SCHOOL TYPE

229mm
1·37m 457mm
457 mm
584mm
229mm 152mm
1·83m

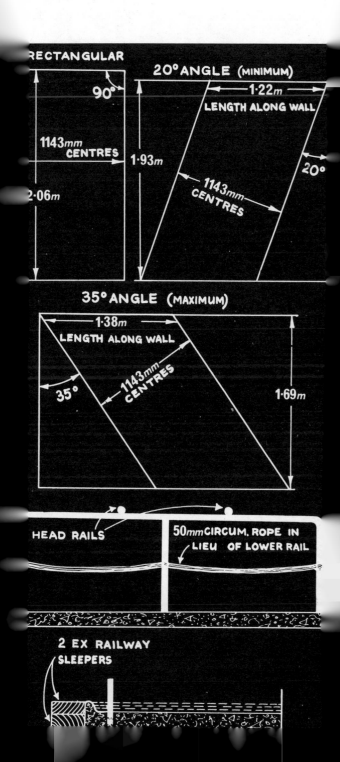

RECTANGULAR

90°

1143mm
CENTRES

2·06m

20° ANGLE (MINIMUM)

1·22m

LENGTH ALONG WALL

1·93m

1143mm
CENTRES

20°

35° ANGLE (MAXIMUM)

1·38m

LENGTH ALONG WALL

1143mm
CENTRES

35°

1·69m

HEAD RAILS

50mm CIRCUM. ROPE IN
LIEU OF LOWER RAIL

2 EX RAILWAY
SLEEPERS

Above: Cows in this double row of kennels have access to a 42·6 m long covered feed passage. The roof of the passage overhangs 2·4 m on either side, enabling the cows to eat in comfort whatever the weather.

Left: Complete diet feeding.

Below, left: Feeding cattle from a Gehl forage box.

Above: Strawed yard in a Crendon wide-span concrete building.

Right: Ayrshire cows at a feed barrier under a lean-to roof on a Shropshire smallholding.

Right: An 80-strong milking herd enjoying a feed of brewers' grains in an open yard.

Slatted floors can increase stock density and reduce capital investment but demand good stockmanship.

systems which operated through the sixties, where large cow numbers were associated with the then currently favoured low-input/low-output system concerning the balance to be achieved between silage and concentrates.

Advantages of the yard-and-parlour systems over the traditional cowshed housing and milking are:

1. The daily requirement of cleaning out the cowshed to meet the requirements of the Milk and Dairy Regulations was reduced to littering the sleeping area of the yard and scraping the loafing and feeding area only. The 'straw yard' would have a deep bed of farmyard manure by the end of the winter period and this could easily be handled by mechanical means in a very short space of time.

2. During the sixties, there was a big move towards more intensive grassland management leading to more intensive stocking rates, i.e. greater cows numbers, which more easily accommodated by the 'yard' system.

3. Self-feed silage was another product of the improving grass technology and this also fitted in with 'loose housing'.

Individual silage feeding was too heavy a task to be contemplated by most farmers still using the cowshed system. With self-feed there must be convenient access to the silage from the yards. The floor of the silage clamp should have a slope of one in twenty away from the silage face to prevent slurry contaminating the lower levels of silage.

4. The parlour milking system had considerable advantages over the cowshed bucket milking system; the recent introduction of circulation cleaning and bulk milk tanks result in greatly improved labour use.

Current thinking suggests that the maximum time that any herdsman should spend in a parlour at any one time is 2–2½ hours. After this period, concentration starts to diminish and attention to detail starts to slip. This is an important consideration to be borne in mind by any farmer thinking about his labour force.

There is a limit to what a well-trained herdsman, who has the responsibility of managing a herd, can be expected to do. Too much time spent on routine tasks certainly takes the edge off the man's husbandry and management skills.

Yard Layout
A yard area should consist of a lying or bedded area and a loafing or feeding area.

The space required for each animal varies depending upon the age and size of stock, the bedded area and feeding system. For adult cows an allowance of $4.2\,m^2$ for lying area and $2.0\,m^2$ for loafing or feeding area is typical. The feeding area gives access to a feed face or a self feed silage area.

The sleeping area must be covered. A feed fence can be situated along the outside of the yard so that feeding can be done by mechanical means, forage boxes, etc. Hay or straw can be conveniently stored adjacent to the yards or on top of the silage clamp.

The principle is to handle all feeds and dung as few times as possible over the shortest possible distance.

Slatted floors can be considered in the loafing area of $2.8-3.4\,m^2$ per head depending upon breed. Slats can be of concrete, up to $3.5\,m$ in length, depth depending upon span $100-225\,mm$, width at top $100-225\,mm$ tapered so that the base is narrower than the top. The recommended width between slats is $25\,mm-40\,mm$. Slatted floor systems reduce bedding and labour cost but are more expensive initially.

With loose housing it is desirable to include in the yard and parlour layout:

- A collecting yard to hold the cows prior to milking with direct access from the yard approaches so that the herd need not enter the yards in summer. Allow $1.2-1.5m^2$ of space per cow depending upon breed with the yard long and preferably narrow at the parlour entrance.
- A diversionary pen at the exit to the parlour with a gate capable of being opened and shut easily by the milker in order to divert any cow needing veterinary attention or for AI as she leaves the parlour.
- A footbath of two sections, one for washing and one for treatment each $2.13\,m \times 1.22\,m$ with a minimum depth of liquid of $150-200\,mm$. Its use is described later.
- A cattle crush for handling cows for brucellosis/tuberculin testing, warble-fly dressing, etc.

Cubicle Housing
The most widespread development in loose housing was the introduction of cow cubicles in a covered yard, or 'cow kennels' with only the lying-in area of the cubicle covered—the latter representing a very low-cost housing system. This system of cow housing is of particular appeal to dairy farmers short of bedding, and has the great advantage of clean cows with the consequent saving in washing time, thus increasing the throughput of cows milked per hour.

Above: This 8-unit rotary tandem milking parlour has a potential of up to 85 cows per man-hour. Such parlours allow for a feeding time during rotation of six minutes.

Below: In this NIRD-designed rotary herringbone layout the partly-opened rump gate guides the entering cow. A sheeted gate covers the manger of the stall through which the cow walks to enter the second stall.

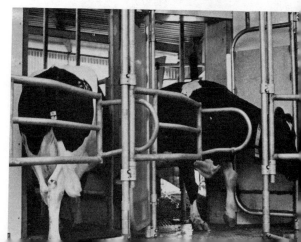

Above: This 20-stall rotary abreast parlour can handle up to 160 cows per hour. The main difference between the abreast and rotary herringbones and tandems is that the operators work from the outside of the platform rather than the inside; the cows face inwards and have to back off the moving platform; and the teat cups are applied between the cows' rear legs.

Right: The 17-stall unit is operated by two men and makes a double rotation. Its platform is pre-set to spend one-third of its cycling time in motion and two-thirds stationary. During the second rotation, because of the odd

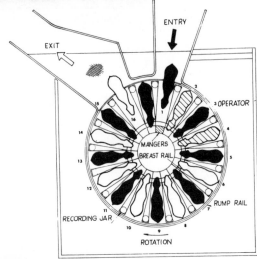

number of stalls, the even numbered stalls stop in front of the entry point to take on cows. As each of these is filled it moves two stalls to the right, where the operator is waiting to apply clusters.

Left: This 14-point rotary herringbone parlour is in the stop position, to allow the next cows onto the platform for milking.

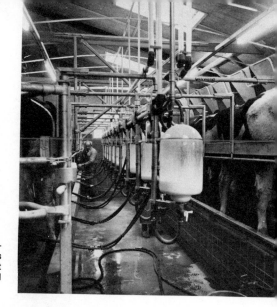

Right: Example of a fixed herringbone parlour; in this installation on a Somerset farm there are 10 units and 20 stalls (10/20).

A new prefabricated herringbone parlour with its circular collection/dispersal yards. The sqeeze gate is weight-operated.

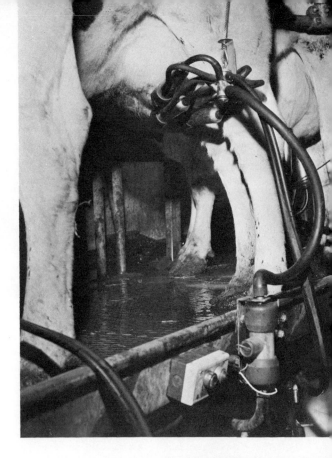

Right: automatic cluster removal in action.

Right: Hosier-Guery's 270 litre glass reinforced plastic mini-vat has a stainless milk vessel and water jacket.

Bulk milk production. As the tank is not kept under vacuum pressure, a weight-operated valve is necessary. When the containers hold a certain quantity of milk, it switches on the motor and cuts out the vacuum so that the milk can be piped into tanks, each of which holds 2455 litres.

This form of dung channel covering is claimed to be clog-free on account of its 72:28 open-to-solid ratio. The pattern of the grid has been set over a basic 1 metre square and comprises stress bars at 127 mm and rounded tread bars at 45 mm, giving 19 bars to a 77 mm run.

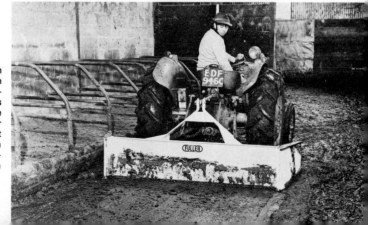

This scraper has a 1·84 m wide main blade fitted with reversible rubber squeegee on its base. Side plates are toed outwards to give 2·13 m sweep and their 1·61 m reach can be set from the tractor seat in a forward position (for pulling) or a backward position for pushing).

Various designs of cubicle are in use and there is less risk of cows refusing to use cubicles if they have plenty of room. The usual length of a cow cubicle is 2·13 m and the width 1·17 m. Where the cubicle is too long a headrail can be used to restrict the length of the bed. The width may have to be varied slightly to fit into the appropriate buildings; the modern farm steel-framed buildings have bays of 4·57 m, which means reducing the width to 1·14 m to fit four cubicles into one bay. The majority of cubicles have two rails along the length. The top rail ideally should be about 1 m above the bed, and the bottom rail about 356 mm above the bed. A recent introduction has been the use of nylon rope as a bottom restraint.

The heelstone is a platform on which the cows stand near the edge so that they dung direct into the passage. The heelstone should be about 228 mm high above the dung passage.

Cubicle beds have posed a perpetual problem. Success has been achieved by filling the cubicle with 'box muck'. This will provide a warm dry lie and if well maintained with straw seems to give cows comfort. Alternatives include rammed chalk, concrete (which can be damp proofed and insulated) and bitumen macadam.

On occasions it is necessary to convert a very narrow building of less than 4·57 m to cubicle use, and in this case it is possible to arrange the cubicles in a herringbone pattern at a minimum of 20° or a maximum of 35° to the passage.

The dung channel between rows of cubicles should have a width of approximately 2·44 m. This may have to be varied according to the requirements of fitting cubicles and passages into existing buildings. The passage needs to be wide enough to allow access to the slurry scraper. Increasingly available are mechanised scrapers pulled by chains, which again would tend to influence the width of the passage. Slatted passages between rows of cubicles eliminate daily scraping, provided the liquid slurry can be handled by tanker or irrigation equipment.

Milking Machines

In machine milking equipment, four distinct types of plant are met with:

1. The bucket type of plant with a tapped overhead fixed vacuum line installed in the cowshed.

2. Pipeline milking, involving a milk pipeline into which the milk is delivered direct from the teat cups without intervening buckets. Recording in this case has to be carried out using a milk-flow meter. There are several approved models on the market. A long

pipeline should have as few vertical lifts and right-angle bends as possible to avoid the risk of a lipase taint which may develop as a result of breakdown of milk fat.

3. The fixed milking parlour or movable milking bail for use with yarded cows or cows at pasture.

4. The rotary system in which cows circulate on a revolving platform past an operator who takes up a standing position.

The principles involved in the parlour and the bail are similar: by centralising milking at one point, the operator's time is saved and the cow does the walking. The operator concentrates on washing and milking the cows in relay and probably feeds the concentrate ration to each cow—all with the minimum of movement on his part.

Conveyance of the milk from the milking points is done by vacuum.

MILKING PARLOURS

The design of milking parlours and equipment has made rapid strides in recent years. The main types of milking parlour available are as follows:

1. Abreast, single-level type in which, as in the original milking bail, cows stand side by side and walk straight through the holding stall when milking ceases. The cows can be raised to ease milking conditions for the operator by a step up to the milking stall of 356–432 mm.

2. Tandem-type parlours, where the cows stand side-on in line to the operator's pit.

3. The chute parlour, a modification of the tandem particularly suitable for narrow buildings in which cows are let in and out in batches.

4. The herringbone parlour, introduced from New Zealand, allows the cows to stand in groups of up to sixteen on one side of the parlour at an angle to the operator's pit, without intervening stall divisions.

5. Rotary parlours—the parlours rotate round or past the operator and incorporate either the tandem, herringbone or abreast principle. The complete rotation is completed in six to seven and a half minutes; movement can be halted by operators while the cows move into their stalls and move out.

Slurry separation.

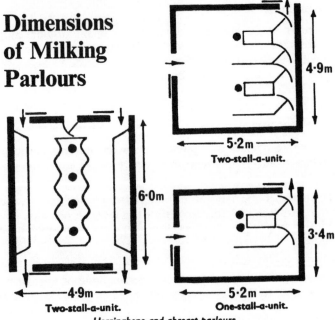

Dimensions of Milking Parlours

4·9m

5·2m

Two-stall-a-unit.

6·0m

4·9m

Two-stall-a-unit.

3·4m

5·2m

One-stall-a-unit.

Herringbone and abreast parlours.

Muck spreading with a sideflinger.

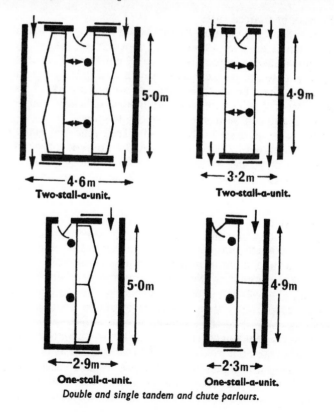

5·0m

◀— 4·6m —▶
Two-stall-a-unit.

4·9m

◀— 3·2m —▶
Two-stall-a-unit.

5·0m

◀— 2·9m —▶
One-stall-a-unit.

4·9m

◀— 2·3m —▶
One-stall-a-unit.

Double and single tandem and chute parlours.

Units of eight, twelve and up to thirty-six stalls are available with throughput up to 150 cows per hour; these are operated by one or two men.

The trend of development is towards automating cluster removal, cow exit and entry control, udder washing and feed control. Also safety stop devices are being incorporated to avoid accidents.

Rotaries were first installed in Britain in 1969. Initially there was considerable interest; however, this has tended to wane, and the larger herringbone parlours have become more popular in the late seventies.

Typical dimensions in terms of the ground plan of these parlours are illustrated in the diagrams on pages 72 and 73.

Before installing a parlour, advice should be obtained from the ADAS Dairy Husbandry Adviser, in order to fit the parlour to the particular conditions of the farm.

Conditions which must be considered are as follows.

1. Feeding of Concentrates

If fed wholly in the parlour, two stalls per milking unit will usually give sufficient time for a cow to eat concentrates. There are considerable variations in the time taken by cows to eat concentrates.

Meal is eaten at a rate between 0·22 and 0·33 kg per minute. Cubes are eaten faster than meal—at something like 0·5 kg per minute. Recent trials with wet feeding have indicated that the rate of food intake can be treble that of dry feeding.

There is an increase in the use of a feed fence on many dairy herds. This allows a division whereby the home-mix type of meal can be fed down the fence and the cubed concentrates ration is then fed in the parlour where there is an obvious limitation on feeding time.

2. Size of Herd

Number of cows per unit falls within the range of ten to fifteen, depending upon layout, yield per cow and spread of calving pattern, if the total time spent in milking is not to exceed one and a half hours in the evening or two hours at morning milking.

The number of units a man can handle without being overtaxed or under employed is then largely governed by what he has to do in milking each cow—the so-called work routine.

In most tandem and abreast parlours the work routine compared with the herringbone routine can be summarised as in Table 3.1. The throughput is shown with reference to each milking system.

The two basic types of parlour have either one stall or two stalls for each milking unit. When two stalls are associated with each

Table 3.1 Work Routine Time

	Time		
Operation	1·25 min. Abreast Tandem Chute	1·0 min. Herringbone Stop/start Rotary	0·80 min. Rotary Tandem— automated door control
1. Let out cow(s)	0·13	0·07	—
Let in cow(s) + feed	0·17	0·13	—
2. Prepare— foremilk	0·12	0·12	0·12
wash and dry	0·20	0·20	0·20
3. Attach cluster	0·20	0·20	0·20
4. Remove cluster	0·15	0·15	0·15
4a. Transfer cluster	(0·35)	(0·35)	—
5. Dip teats	0·08	0·08	0·08
6. Walking	0·15	—	—
7. Miscellaneous tasks	0·05	0·05	0·05
Total	1·25	1·00	0·80
Maximum cows per man per hour	48	60	75

(*Choice of Milking Parlours*, MAFF)

milking unit it is possible to feed and prepare the newly entered cow while the unit is on the other cow in the paired stall. This type allows full use of the milking units and a longer feeding time for each cow. Where there is a unit for each stall, the unit will be idle while the cow is replaced and the newly entered cow is fed and prepared.

The feeding time is limited to the preparation and milking-out time in abreast and tandem parlours, and to the cow's circuit time in the rotary type of parlour.

In herringbone parlours the cows are handled in batches and occupy stalls during batch preparation time and the longest time taken by any cow in the batch to milk out. The feeding time then is likely to be quite long.

The potential throughput of cows in any type of parlour is influenced by the time required for the cows to milk out, the number of milking units and the length of the work routine.

In the cases of low-yielding cows, the limiting factor on throughput will be the work routine. In the case of high-yielding cows the time for the cows to milk out is the limiting factor, which should give the milker ample time to carry out a full routine.

3. Available Buildings

The third consideration is whether an existing building can be adapted to house the type of parlour chosen or whether to build afresh. Whatever decision is made must take into account the need for proper siting of the parlour in relation to the yards to allow easy passage of cows both into and from the parlour.

Cost of Parlours—Dairy Buildings

A typical cubicle house with a central feeding passage, with cubicle house lean-to on either side with dung passages, etc. would cost approximately £500 to £700 per cow place. The building to house a milking parlour, herringbone or rotary, would cost between £7000 and £11,500. The parlour equipment to go into the building would range from £11,500 to £30,000 per point, according to size and degree of sophistication.

The bulk tank could be installed at a charge of £5–8 per litre stored inclusive of all fittings.

Where buildings exist it may be possible to equip them for a slightly lower price. But unless they at least cover the same sort of area per cow as is being sold in unit construction form, it is doubtful whether the same sort of economies in labour would be achieved and conversion costs can be high.

Collection of Milk

All milk was collected from farms in England and Wales by tanker as from July 1979. All milk collected from farms in Scotland is collected from farm tanks and transported in road tankers.

To join a collection scheme, a farmer must install a refrigerated milk vat (tank) which complies with a specification laid down by the boards. At the time of the collection, the tanker driver inspects the milk in the vat, checks the temperature, agitates the milk and takes a sample for testing under the various schemes controlling the quality of the milk. The quantity is measured either by a dipstick and a calibration chart or by use of a flowmeter.

The premium bulk tank scheme finished in all the Scottish Board areas by 1979. In England and Wales, the premium is payable per litre according to the size of tank and over a period of three years after the date of last installation which was July 1979.

Calf Housing

Calves should be housed in a building which, above all, can be kept warm and draught free: good hygienic conditions are also important. They are best housed in individual pens with solid partition walls to reduce draughts; if housed in groups of up to four calves, yoke fittings or straps fastened to rings in the wall of the pen are advisable to enable each calf to be individually fed.

Hay racks should be made movable (feeding the hay in nets is an alternative); a water bowl in each pen is desirable. A floor area of approximately $1·2\,\text{m} \times 1·8\,\text{m}$ is needed for each calf.

Young cattle below twelve months old require winter accommodation in the form of a yard either semi- or fully covered with ample trough and rack room—between 450 mm and 550 mm per animal.

It is wise to have temporary divisions in such yards to allow calves to be grouped according to size, thus reducing bullying. Such yards need not be elaborate in construction as long as they provide a dry bed and allow a minimum area of $4\,\text{m}^2$ per animal.

Bulling heifers and in-calf heifers may be out-wintered on many farms but, if in-wintered, yarding accommodation as above (but allowing $5·6\,\text{m}^2$ per beast) is required.

Dung and Slurry

In earlier housing methods it was usual for the dung to be removed from cowhouses on a regular daily basis. With new housing systems and mechanisation it is more likely that the bedded area on a loose-housed system will be cleared out once per year, usually by contract, and slurry is likely to have been pushed into a slurry lagoon or tower, again to be emptied at leisure when other farm jobs are not pressing. This is often carried out on a contractual basis.

With the energy crisis and the increase in fertiliser prices, it is increasingly important to realise the value of the plant nutrients in dung and slurry and to use it as effectively as possible.

The amounts of dung (i.e. faeces plus urine) which an animal voids in a year (assuming housed all year) would be in the order of 14,600 litres, containing an approximate value of 51 kg nitrogen, 16 kg phosphate and 84 kg potash.

In the form of slurry the value per 10 m^3 would be 35 kg nitrogen, 11 kg phosphate and 58 kg potash.

Pastures for grazing would be top-dressed during the early winter when the frosty ground was hard and suitable for travel.

During the months of June and July, dressings could be applied to aftermaths and for ploughing into seedbeds for kale and maize. There could be a health risk from Johne's disease or salmonellosis. So it is best not to graze young stock on slurry-treated grassland.

Statutory Requirements

It should be noted that before work commences on erection of new buildings or the extension of old certain consents may be necessary.

Although, within certain limits, development for agricultural purposes is 'permitted development', beyond these limits planning permission will be required. All buildings must comply with national Building Regulations but for agriculture there is some exemption.

If disposal of foul drainage is involved then the consent of the local authority and water authority may be required.

Work must also meet the requirements of the Milk and Dairies Regulations where appropriate and also the Health and Safety at Work Act 1974.

There are also other consents which may be necessary and where there is doubt the appropriate authority should be consulted or your ADAS adviser can assist.

Building Standards

British Standard SS02
This is the code of practice for the Design of Buildings and Structure for Agriculture. It:
- brings together in a single standard much already available information;
- gives recommendations for the design, construction and provision of service to agricultural buildings;
- is performance based in designing to a particular site;
- recognises four classes of buildings in terms of design life, period

and density of human occupancy and proximity to highways and dwellings;

● is available in three parts from the British Standards Institution.

In cases of doubt professional advice will be required but where contractors are used they may well be familiar with the requirement. ACILG (Agricultural Construction Industry Liaison Group) maintains a register of those members who have undertaken to conform to the relevant sections.

Grant Aid

Buildings and fixed equipment may qualify for grant aid under UK or EEC schemes administered by MAFF. Rates and conditions vary according to policy current at a particular time. Prior approval each individual time is not required but work must comply with various requirements. In particular work must be of a 'capital nature'; work carried out to the requirements of BS SS02 will be deemed to satisfy this particular test.

For details consult the nearest Divisional Office of the Ministry of Agriculture.

CHAPTER 4

THE SYSTEM SHOULD SUIT THE FARM

GENERAL ORGANISATION

IN the British Isles, dairy farming was first based on the production of milk for sale as butter and cheese rather than as liquid milk. Cows calved naturally in the spring and the bulk of their milk produced during the summer was manufactured into cheese and butter which was easily sold to the rapidly developing industrial areas in the country at the turn of the century. This occurrence was in largely grassland areas, e.g. Cheshire and Somerset.

There was an increasing demand for fresh milk and this was originally supplied by town dairies. It was this setting up of town dairies which was the reason for the introduction of black and white cattle from Holland. The indigenous cattle, mainly of the Shorthorn type, were found not to be as suitable for the increasing demand for higher levels of milk production.

Transport facilities improved, both rail and road, and this largely destroyed the advantage that certain dairy farms had of being located near to a consuming centre.

The advent of the milk marketing boards in October 1933 put a bottom into the market and made available a transport system which enabled milk to be taken to any appropriate market, be it for liquid or manufacturing use and irrespective of where in the country it was produced.

The growth of dairy farming was also aided by the availability of imported feeding stuffs for at least fifty years prior to the Second World War. Farms were by no means self-sufficient; the home-produced maintenance foods, e.g. hay, roots and straw, were easily and cheaply supplemented by imported cereals and oil cakes from overseas.

Thus, dairy farming in this country developed largely as a pro-

80

cessing industry. The dairy farmer was concerned not so much with growing and feeding his own crops as with the conversion of purchased feeding stuffs into milk. Only by such a system could dairy farming have survived the bleak conditions of East Lancashire, the West Riding or Lanarkshire.

Small farms in these areas produced large quantities of milk from the use of cheap imported feeding stuffs. The system did provide a means of building up fertility on these farms which would have been impossible if the farms had to be dependent solely on their own farm resources. The system which was evolved concentrated very much on milk production; few herd replacements were reared as there was a plentiful supply of down-calving heifers from more remote livestock rearing areas. This availability of replacements also encouraged farmers to sell off cows at the end of a lactation for beef, thus providing another cheap source of food to the industrial areas, particularly in the North of England.

Descriptive phrases, such as 'Flying Herd', 'Milk and Feed', are still used today in these traditional dairying areas. During and since the Second World War the pendulum has swung in the opposite direction. During the war availability of imported feeds was greatly restricted, giving great incentive to self-sufficiency on the dairy farm. In more recent years prices of imported feeds have risen steeply and this further emphasises the continuing need for increasing self-sufficiency on the dairy farm. In practical terms this necessitates a much greater exploitation of the farm resources available. All dairy farms have a similar range of basic resources—cows, grassland, buildings and labour.

Success in dairying will only be achieved by blending these resources to achieve the maximum profit available. There is a different recipe for success for every farm. On any given farm, the climate, the area of land available and its inherent fertility play a considerable part in deciding which system of dairy farming is to be followed.

A factor which contributed to the spread of dairying for liquid milk production was its relatively greater profitability than butter or cheese production, although these had, as ancillary enterprises, the rearing of stock and pig fattening.

Butter and cheese prices are subject to world competition. The relative freedom of fresh milk from this competition together with the work of the marketing boards and Treasury subsidies which encouraged milk consumption, ensured that milk sold on the liquid market in the United Kingdom always commanded a much better price than that available from milk used for manufacturing purposes.

Many marginal farms changed over to a milk-producing system because of its greater profitability and its regular return.

In more recent years there have been various schemes made available to persuade the producers to return to livestock rearing and beef production. As a member of the EEC the fact that there exists a surplus of manufactured milk products in the EEC is likely to ensure that such conversion schemes will remain with us, together with the possibilities of other schemes which will be launched in the future to curtail the amount of milk being produced in the EEC.

To illustrate the general organisation of dairy farming, examples will be shown of small, medium and large farms to show how land is the dominant factor in deciding the size of the dairying enterprise and the part it plays in the economy of the farm.

1. Small Dairy Farms: 10–40 Hectares

These are generally situated on vale land of above-average fertility, typical of the western parts of Britain, mainly in grass. If they are arable holdings they are usually associated with market gardening rather than cereal production. Owing to limited areas, stocking rates per hectare need to be fairly intensive, somewhere in the region of 1·89–2·24 cows per hectare.

With the increasing emphasis on grass and grass products these levels of stocking must be related to a fairly high level of nitrogen application. The higher stocking rates, coupled with the necessary higher levels of fertiliser, particularly nitrogen, inevitably lead to a need for the reorganisation of the type of winter forage used, and on most farms this has resulted in a changeover from hay to silage. Bearing in mind that the basic factors of production on any farm are land, labour and capital, so on these farms a shortage of land can only result in the farm necessarily becoming much more labour- and capital-intensive. Labour is often provided on the small farm by the family unit so in the interests of more production from the farm, capital needs to be invested in silage making equipment. Numerous schemes have been available for grants towards the cost of providing both machinery and suitable buildings to enable small farmers to move into this area of intensive grass technology.

A major reason which persuaded many farmers into this policy was of course the vulnerability of small farms to the vagaries of the climate when they were dependent upon hay as the main fodder crop for winter feeding of cows. Barn-dried hay is made on some farms but still does not provide a safeguard against unpredictable weather.

The emphasis in small-scale farming must be on achieving a high output per hectare, and this can only be achieved by coupling intensive stocking rates with a high level of output per cow. In order to maintain a high output of milk, only sufficient young stock are reared to meet replacement needs. The question as to the need for rearing young stock on the small farm needs to be fully investigated.

On some farms there may be small marginal areas, very hilly and suitable for little else, but normally young stock rearing involves the investment of capital with no immediate return which makes heavy demands upon cash-flow. Additionally, land put to rearing stock could alternatively be used to maintain a cow in milk production which would certainly contribute to the farm profits.

Small farms are in the main run as family farms or with no more than one hired man. Rents are usually high and the farms tend to be equipped with buildings, silage barns, feed fences, which all add up to a very high level of fixed costs.

It is therefore essential that there must be a high output per hectare to cover the fixed costs. Small farms have to be very well managed and there is little scope for error.

2. Medium-Sized Dairy Farms: 40–101 Hectares

In contrast to the highly specialised small dairy farms previously described, medium-sized farms run dairy herds not usually as the hub of the farming system but rather as a component of a mixed farming economy.

These farms are large enough to run other livestock enterprises such as meat production (beef or mutton) in addition to the dairy herd. They are also able to devote arable land to cash crops, whereas the small farmer cannot afford to grow cash crops at the expense of his fodder supplies. Even so on these medium-sized farms there is a trend towards specialisation and fewer, larger enterprises. In this more streamlined situation there is scope for the development of a high level of enterprise efficiency which brings together the aspects of some economy of scale coupled with the employment of a profit-orientated professional work-force.

A greater availability of land is likely to make available areas where young stock rearing could be carried on, so self-contained herds can be maintained. If this is run in conjunction with a profitable dairy unit, the sale of surplus quality stock becomes an interesting possibility.

The size of the dairy herd on farms in this medium-sized group is governed initially by the availability of grazing land for intensive management. This would be reconciled with the arable area so

that a balanced farm rotation could be worked out. Over many
years, high-level dairy farming has shown better and more consistent profits to the farmer than any other farm enterprise. Therefore, in most situations the dairy unit has progressively become
the more important enterprise even on the medium-sized mixed
farm.

3. Dairying on Large Farms: 101 Hectares and Over

Extensive farming, assessed in terms of land availability, has long
been associated with the corn-growing areas of southern and eastern England. The description 'sheep and barley' land gives an
insight into the type of farming systems practised. Light-land farms,
where the soil was not inherently fertile had a continuing need of
livestock to provide a means of cashing the necessary grass or root
break which put fertility and structure back into the soil. Profits
from sheep declined rapidly over the years, and they were replaced
by dairying in many areas such as the Wiltshire downs where
extensive dairying ousted cereal growing as well. An important
part of this development was the introduction of the milking bail.

The large farms did offer considerable scope for a widely diver-
sified system of farming including cereals, seed production, milk,
beef or mutton. However, in more recent years there has been a
significant trend to simplification, involving in many cases just
cereals and dairying, the latter being in covenient viable units of
about one hundred cows. Stocking rates tend not to be too intensive, round about 1·8–2·0 cows per hectare.

Many of the herds had the advantage of being started from a
bare site, the buildings that were erected being simple and very
functional. In many cases it was possible to set up a herd based
on the 'block calving' system, which eased management and
allowed the units to be designed for a one-man work-force with
appropriate relief. The feeding emphasis was on growing and
utilising as much grass as possible. Due to the vulnerability of
downland areas to dry summers there has tended to be a move
towards an autumn calving pattern. Late lactation cows are not hit
as hard by a shortage of summer grass.

No Standard Pattern

From the brief description of the dairying systems given, it is
apparent that there is no standard pattern for a dairy farm. Between
the extremes of intensive dairying on typically small or family
farms and extensive dairying with greater emphasis on output per
man, there is every opportunity to make use of the locally occurring

resources which are available; the main requirement is the skill of the dairy farmer to achieve the best blend of resources to match the local conditions and to achieve the highest possible profit level.

One last factor in the system of farming needs to be considered—the choice of breed and type of cow within that breed to fit the farm and type of farming pursued. The main factors to be considered when choosing the type of cow for the system could be considered as follows.

Stocking Rate

Stocking rate depends upon a consideration of two basic features—(i) the fertility of the soil, and (ii) the size of cow.

The area of land required to provide the maintenance requirement for a cow is also very much related to the level of fertiliser input. Nitrogen application on intensive dairy farms has crept up over the years so that on most progressive farms it now has reached the 250–300 kg N/hectare level.

The various breeds of cows have a varying requirement of land per cow. Examples of average stocking rates for the leading breeds are provided in Table 4.1.

Table 4.1. **Average stocking rates**

Breed	Average liveweight (kg)	Cows per hectare
Jerseys	356	3·33
Guernseys ⎫ Ayrshire ⎬	457	2·2
Friesians	559	2·08
Holsteins	660	1·78

On land of the same fertility more Jerseys than any other breed could be kept on the same area of land. There are, however, other considerations concerning the amount of production required from the land above the maintenance requirement. This varies from the extensive low-output systems requiring perhaps 8–9 tonne silage per cow per winter, plus summer grazing, compared with the system of high output per cow on limited area where only maintenance requirements are supplied from the land and all production rations brought in. This can approximate to the town dairy of many years ago. These latter considerations have as great an effect on stocking rate as does the choice of cattle breed.

Intensive stocking rates do tend to encourage internal parasites such as worms but modern routine animal health treatments tend to control this problem.

Poaching of pastures by intensive stocking does present a problem in wet seasons, particularly in the spring and autumn. Some form of zero grazing at these times is beneficial, providing the buildings allow such practices and the appropriate equipment is available.

The need for labour is closely related to the number of cows, so to save labour there has tended to be a move towards the higher-yielding breeds of cow.

Breed Specialisation

It has been already pointed out that in terms of land use, milk production in this country has given a greater income than meat production. This has resulted in intensive selection for milk, the traditional dual-purpose breeds—Shorthorn, Lincoln Red, Red Poll—being greatly reduced in numbers. They have been replaced by the Friesian which, however, has some merit in producing a very suitable beef calf when mated to virtually any of the pure beef breeds—Hereford, Angus, Charolais or Limousin.

High Butterfat Breeds

The compositional quality of milk is becoming increasingly important, and the Channel Island breeds are noted for their high butterfat contents. The new scale of milk payments based on better quality will tend to press this point in particular. There are, however, good quality levels available in the high-yielding breeds, and, provided that cows are fed adequately, then each herd will realise its quality potential, which has not always been the case in the past.

Yield and quality of milk are now recorded on national milk records, and any producer who wishes to monitor both in his herd certainly has the tools to do this.

The Cow as a Consumer of Roughage

The continuing interest in greater self-sufficiency on dairy farms means that the cow will be expected to consume a high proportion of largely roughage foods at appropriate times in the lactation. These home-grown foods are generally more fibrous and bulky than concentrate foods and therefore in the future it is very important that cows will consume and *effectively* utilise these increasing quantities of farm-produced foods. The ability to do this is not the prerogative of any one breed; it is a quality present within all breeds and it is most important that this characteristic should be looked for, identified and bred for in future cow generations. This implies a detailed knowledge of individual cow performance and reinforces the need for recording and monitoring both individual and herd performance.

Cow Observation
The cow that grazes with relish and milks consistently well on pasture alone is the cow to be preferred to the one that needs supplementary feeding on the same pasture to maintain similar milk yields. Cows exhibit a wide variation in their ability in this respect. The dairy cow has a great adaptability to environment. Some breeds are credited with the ability to live under adverse conditions; others are said to need more favourable conditions. In recent years these ideas have been confounded by the wide dispersal of all breeds.

It must be realised that fundamentally milk production has to be fed for, and this must be considerably in excess of the bare subsistence afforded by traditional feeding arrangements. With adequate feeding any group of cows will perform to the point where they will achieve their genetic potential. The successful dairy farmer of the future will make sure that he attains not the genetic yield potential of his herd, but rather the optimal yield level coupled with the maximum profit available. Local affiliations to any one breed should not be lightly discarded; surplus stock is more readily sold in areas where the breed concerned is in popular favour. It is not always profitable to initiate change, but alternatively a head in the sand attitude allows the world to change without notice.

CHAPTER 5

CROPPING POLICY ON DAIRY FARMS

FROM the middle sixties, the cropping of dairy farms has been planned to achieve a much higher degree of self-sufficiency. Imported feeds have become progressively more and more expensive and the balance of payments has to be considered; hence the need for some economy in livestock food imports.

There has been a continuing emphasis on the need to produce from our own farm resources by successive governments. This policy has been closely associated with modern grassland techniques involving heavy nitrogen dressing, various forms of intensive grazing to ensure efficient grassland utilisation coupled with more efficient grassland conservation systems for winter fodder.

Larger herd size has led to more intensive stocking rates. The overall tendency has been to an intensification of land use.

When planning the cropping on a dairy farm, the first consideration is to decide upon the size of the herd and the policy concerning herd replacements. This matter has been mentioned before, but to recap briefly, it is important for a small farmer to keep the largest number of milking cows on the farm coupled with the smallest number of replacement stock. Contract rearing of heifers helps in this aim, and in many cases all replacements are bought in. The usual replacement rate on dairy herds is between 20 and 25 per cent. The lower level of this range must be aimed for, but in budgeting terms a 25 per cent level would be reasonable (so that a herd of one hundred cows would require twenty-five heifer replacements each year.) Using the normally accepted livestock equivalents, this would mean approximately one hectare devoted to followers for every three cows. Where feeding for the replacement heifers includes straw and purchased supplements this ratio can be increased. With an average calving age of two and half years, a 'replacement unit' of one calf, one yearling and a heifer would equal about 1·4 livestock units.

Once a decision has been reached on the total number of cows and followers needed, the cropping must be planned taking into account other considerations. These are as follows.

Situation of Farm

Choose crops which fit in with the soil and climatic conditions. Generally speaking the western parts of Britain are more favourable to the growth of grass and root crops; the eastern areas to cereal crops. High elevation tends to restrict cultivations: upland areas have a shallow depth of soil and climate, which allows crops to grow but does not necessarily allow harvesting. Late spring with early winter give a very short growing season and restrict choice of crops. Heavier rainfall on higher land requires better drainage, which is not possible where the soil has little depth and overlies rock.

Size of Farm

The smaller the farm the greater the need for raising output per hectare of land to the maximum. This is where type of soil, soil fertility and skill in cultivation play an important part. Where the land is well drained and free working, the use of the short-term leys coupled with catch cropping (e.g. kale or stubble turnips) is possible and such a policy would intensify land use and help considerably towards self-sufficiency.

Capital Resources

The amount of working capital required for the purchase of seeds and fertiliser and the capital required to finance the appropriate machinery will govern the range of crops grown. The rise in machinery costs in particular, both capital and running costs, have escalated to such high levels in the late seventies that there is considerable incentive to consider the co-operative owning of machinery and resources. Very favourable schemes are available administered by the Central Council for Agricultural and Horticultural Co-operation. This is a well-established method of coping with the need for capital much employed by farmers in the EEC countries; Holland and France in particular.

Many small dairy farms tend to be over-capitalised in machinery and it could be that in many cases use could be made of contract services. Objections to contractors tend to be concerned with availability and timeliness of operation. In the majority of cases these problems can be overcome provided contracts are placed early enough and that prompt payment for work is guaranteed.

With interest on borrowed money having risen to 15–20 per cent, the arguments for a small farmer to own all his own machines have become less convincing.

Labour

Apart from the labour requirements of individual crops there is need in planning to choose a sequence of crops which give an even spread of labour during the growing season.

Table 5.1. Energy Costs of Feedingstuffs

Crop	Average yield/ha kg of DM	ME	Total yield MJ/ha	Cost per ha £	Market value per tonne (1980) £	Cost of energy Production cost pence per MJ	Cost of energy Market value cost pence per MJ
Grazed grass	7180	11·0	78,980	225	—	0·28	—
Grass silage	8160	10·0	81,000	358	—	0·44	—
Hay	4270	8·0	34,160	202	—	0·60	—
Maize silage	9040	10·8	97,632*	437	—	0·45	—
Dried grass	—	11·0	9460*	—	95	—	1·00
Kale (direct drilled)	5600	11·0	61,600	220	—	0·36	—
Straw (barley)	—	7·3	6278*	—	25	—	0·4
Winter oats	3870	11·5	44,505	340	90	0·76	0·91
Spring barley	3870	13·7	53,019	340	95	0·64	0·81
Winter barley	4085	13·7	55,964	345	95	0·62	0·81
Winter wheat	4300	14·0	60,200	365	100	0·61	0·83
High energy concentrates	—	13·5	11,610*	—	144	—	1·25
Medium energy concentrates	—	12·5	10,750*	—	132	—	1·23

* MJ calculated on a per tonne basis.
(Kindly provided by Farm Advisory Service Agricultural Division, ICI.)

A small area of a high-labour demanding crop (e.g. roots) may be justified if it offers employment at otherwise relatively slack periods. Where labour is employed solely on the dairy unit it is possible for one man to cope with the everyday tasks—milking, feeding, slurry disposal—of running a 100-cow unit.

This leaves little time for the equally important aspects of cow management and time off. A reasonable figure of one man per sixty cows is more acceptable; as units become larger so the task of marshalling groups of cows, breeding management and group feeding take up a greater proportion of time. If the unit is to be profitable, these tasks must not be skimped. Where the dairy unit is on a large farm, the provision of grass, grass conservation and supply of fodder crops tend to be the responsibility of the arable staff. It is important that the arable team appreciates the importance of producing good-quality fodder on the farm and how important their efforts are in securing these quality end-products.

Economy of Production

The final criterion in planning any system of cropping is to grow those crops which provide the cheapest source of nutrients for the dairy cow.

In general the conclusion to be drawn from Table 5.1 is the relative cheapness of the grazed crops; conservation of grass as silage or hay tends to double the cost.

Obviously, therefore, the cropping of any dairy farm requires a carefully thought out plan in relation to the size of farm, cropping potential of the land and economic use of time and machinery available.

Streamlining Production

The trend in farm organisation has been towards streamlining production to those enterprises best suited to the farm and ensuring that each enterprise is appropriately capitalised. On small farms (40 hectares) in high-rainfall areas, this trend has taken the form of increased specialisation on grass.

Better management and fertiliser usage have increased stock-carrying capacity, leading to larger dairy herds which require more accommodation.

To capitalise such expansion in milk production has often meant cutting out other small livestock enterprises and saving on arable equipment by not growing cereals. This has led to a shortage of straw for litter, but the use of sawdust and shavings, cubicles and slatted floors offer solutions to the litter problem.

Similarly, on larger farms, herds have increased in size to become economically viable, but the choice of foods to grow for the dairy herd is much wider.

In lower-rainfall areas, cereal growing, kale and sugar beet offer cheap sources of winter feed without the problem of litter becoming acute. Such diversity of cropping allows the steady employment throughout the year of a constant labour force. Typical cropping schedules for these various type of farms are available.

CROPPING PLANS

These cropping schedules (Tables 5.2 and 5.3) illustrate the dominance of grass on the smaller farms and the integration of leys with cash cropping on the larger farms. Rainfall and soil type set the pattern of cropping within the farm.

Table 5.2. Small farm (24 hectares) stocking 40 cows (flying herd)

| | Rainfall over 76 cm | | Rainfall under 76 cm | |
Cropping	Heavy land	Light land	Heavy land	Light land
Medium-term leys (5 years)				
Timothy, meadow fescue	12	8	8	8
Ryegrass dominant	8	12	4	4
Lucerne (conservation)	—	—	8	8
Forage crops				
Winter rye/maize	4	—	4	—
Winter rye/kale or Italian rye/ kale	—	4	—	4

Rotation: four years' ley—catch crops—direct re-seed (maiden seeds)

Modern fixed equipment such as buildings, roads and water supplies contribute toward more efficient use of labour but do not necessarily mean reduced feed costs, unless they are allied to land sufficient in area and fertility to produce the necessary supply of high-quality bulk fodder. The intensive use of fertilisers on small intensively managed paddocks has been heavily exploited in recent years in order to provide the necessary quality bulk.

In the arable situation grass plays a much less important role in feeding the cow. There has been an interest in the system of keeping cows housed all the year round, without any grass grazed in situ. Livestock production on the 'Beef-Lots' of America demonstrate this possibility. Large herds, over three hundred cows,

Table 5.3. Medium-sized farm (80 hectares) stocking 60 cows and 30 followers.

	Rainfall over 76 cm		Rainfall under 76 cm	
Cropping	Heavy land	Light land	Heavy land	Light land
Three-year leys				
Timothy, meadow fescue	20	10	10	10
Ryegrass dominant	10	20	10	10
Lucerne (for conservation)	—	—	10	10
Forage Crops				
Winter rye/maize	4	—	4	—
Winter rye or Italian rye/kale	—	4	—	4
Cash Roots				
Potatoes or sugar beet	6	6	6	6
Cereals	40	40	40	40

Rotation: three years' ley—cereal–cereal—root and forage crops—cereal–cereal (undersown)

would possibly justify the use of mechanical feeding by spreading the cost of mechanisation. Certainly the grazing of large cow herds is much affected by the problems of poaching in wet weather. This wastes grass and hampers grass regrowth by ruining soil texture. During the seventies, several large herds were set up but all seem to have run into the practical difficulties associated with large numbers.

Management of these large herds has not been tight enough, and with machinery costs escalating, the systems rapidly become economically suspect. Large herds were put on to many arable farms so that they could utilise the grass break put in to promote soil structure and fertility on intensive cereal blocks. In future large herds on arable farms may be fed on processed straw. It is not certain that grass will play such an important part on these farms as it has done in the past.

On the western side of the country, with a 'milk from grass' policy, the size of herd as a grazing unit will tend to limit the optimum herd size to between sixty and ninety cows. Where herds have increased to between 120 and 150 cows it is essential to split the herd into two, depending upon the calving pattern. The dry cows could be split off and could be grazing behind the milk cows on a paddock system. In-calf heifers could also run with the dry cow group. Block calving herds will perhaps be grazed as one herd, but the grazing system is more likely to be 'set stocking', possibly less intensive and more able to cope with the poaching problem.

The price of concentrates has risen considerably during recent years, e.g. from £36 to £135 per tonne in eight years. This has had the effect of focusing efforts on the following:

- a more efficient growing of grass and conservation as silage or hay;
- possible extension of the grazing season autumn and spring, for the appropriate groups of cattle.

Bearing in mind these considerations, the next two chapters will deal with arable crops and grass as feed for the dairy cow.

CHAPTER 6

BEST CROPS TO GROW ON DAIRY FARMS

THE previous chapter dealt with the planning of food requirements for the dairy herd in terms of crops best fitted to the different circumstances on individual farms. There is no general answer to be given to this matching of stock, crop and farm. Each farm is a unique problem which is capable of one best solution.

Guidance is now given on the growing of arable crops and their utilisation. Grass will be considered separately later.

Raising crop yields per hectare should be the aim of all farmers. Heavier applications of fertilisers and a more comprehensive knowledge of their value and use would have this effect on most farms.

The first essential is a knowledge of the existing soil fertility status. A soil analysis survey can be undertaken by various organisations which can then be translated into action to meet any deficiencies that have been identified. Good and carefully timed cultivations contribute their part; full advantage should be taken of weather conditions. An attempt must be made to work with nature, for instance ploughing heavy land in early winter to achieve a frost tilth which will provide a good seed bed. A firm but well-worked seed bed, providing adequate aeration of the soil, is to be coupled with the fineness of seed bed which must be related to the size of seed going in. A close contact between seed and soil particles is desirable. Good arable crops require that sufficient attention is paid to liming and draining. There has been much encouragement by way of Government grants over past years.

CEREAL CROPS

Barley
There has been a considerable increase in barley area since the mid-fifties. At that time intensive beef systems were developed

95

using large amounts of barley, and because of its higher energy value, it—to a great extent—completely replaced oats as a source of energy for the ruminant.

This trend was greatly accelerated by the work of plant breeders who paid considerable attention to the characteristics of yield, strength of straw and ability to respond to higher levels of fertiliser application. Additional factors such as better field equipment

Table 6.1. Crop Areas

Crop	Area '000 ha	per cent total area
Wheat	1357	7·2
Barley	2343	12·4
Oats	155	0·8
Other grain	23	0·1
Total	3878	20·5
Potatoes	208	1·1
Sugar beet	212	1·1
Oilseed rape	77	0·4
Horticulture	282	1·5
Other crops and fallow	330	1·7
Total tillage	4987	26·3
Temporary grass (under 5 years old)	1986	10·5
Total arable	6973	36·8
Permanent grass (5 years old and over)	5132	27·1
Rough grazing	6361	33·6
Other land	485	2·5
	18,951	100·00

(*Management Pocketbook*, J. Nix.)

including more efficient combines and the more widespread use of chemical sprays all helped to promote the increase in barley area. Averages for 1978–80 (June) were as shown in Table 6.1.

Cereal growing affords an example of the economies to be gained from an increasing scale of operations. In the specialist cereal areas there was a trend to continuous cropping with cereals. But such extreme specialisation is not necessary on a dairy farm where a grass ley can constitute a profitable break to cereal growing.

The barley crop does offer to the dairy farmer an opportunity of providing a high-energy food in terms of grain and additionally an amount of straw which can not only be used for litter but also for feeding. Recently developments in the processing of straw by alkali treatment have opened up considerable scope for use of treated straw and also in harvesting and processing as 'whole crop'.

When analysed under the gross margin system, barley was shown to have a better gross margin than many livestock enterprises (excluding dairy cows) and this, coupled with the lower level of fixed costs required, again helped to encourage the expansion of the barley area. In recent years, this comparatively strong position has been held.

With barley grain and processed straw being so readily available on the large farms, it is possible that grass will play a less important part on dairy/arable farms in the future than in the past. Dairying has in recent years been the most profitable way of cashing the grass break but this may not always be so.

There have been developments in the processing of feeding barley and straw to make them more useful in livestock feeding.

1. Moist barley storage became popular during the early seventies. This can be taken direct from the combine within the moisture range of 18–24 per cent; after rolling it can be used for feed, with none of the drying costs associated with conventional grain storage at 14 per cent moisture. The rising cost of the towers has greatly restricted interest in this method of storage.

2. The processing of straw, i.e. treatment of straw by caustic soda, seems to offer considerable scope for the future. By treatment of this type the digestibility of straw is improved by up to 75 per cent, which makes the straw comparable to average-good hay although obviously lacking in protein. The process is carried out on both an industrial and a farm scale. Processed straw could play an important part in feeding dairy cows in the future.

In the successful growing of barley for feed, yield is so important. The main features to be observed are, firstly, early ploughing: drill into a frost mould if possible at a depth of 3·8–5·1 cm, as soon as soil conditions permit in the spring. Secondly correct soil acidity should be maintained by adequate liming: fertiliser application up to 80 units N, 40 units P_2O_5, 40 units K_2O, and seed rates 125–157 kg/hectare should be sufficient on good tilths.

Suitable varieties of barley recommended generally by NIAB:

winter barley: Maris Otter, Sonja, Igri, Hoppel and Athene;
spring barley: Georgie, Athos, Sundance, Tyra, Ark Royal, Lofa Abed, Mazurka and Aramir.

Oats

There has been a great reduction in the amount of oats grown since the mid-sixties, almost completely due to the growing interest in barley. The cause of this was the fact that oats have a smaller energy content than barley, and there was the problem also that most oat varieties had long straw and were not suited to the expected work rate of the modern combine harvester. Plant breeders gave much attention to the selection of yield and short straw strength which seemed to have more potential in barley than in the oat crop. However, with better feeding of the dairy cow, it is thought that too much barley can be fed to a cow, and oats do offer a very useful alternative. The higher level of fibre in oats takes on a new importance when cows are subjected to high-energy diets.

Oat straw traditionally was thought to have a better feeding value than other cereal straws. This was really explained by the fact that oats, grown in the western half of the United Kingdom, were usually harvested early before all the nutrients were translocated from the straw up to the ear.

Oats are able to tolerate a higher degree of soil acidity than barley. Continuous cropping, however, does offer the possibility of cereal root eel-worm infection.

Suitable varieties of oats recommended for general use by NIAB:

winter oats: Pennal, Maris Osprey and Peniarth;
spring oats: Maris Oberon, Leanda and Maris Tabard.

Wheat

When grown on the dairy farm, wheat is considered to be a very good means of cashing the stored up fertility present in grassland. The straw is generally used for bedding. The winter wheat varieties are harvested quite early in the season and provide a suitable entry into the rotation for a fodder catch crop and the autumn establishment of a new ley.

With the heavier yield and better price, wheat has the highest gross margins of the cereal crops.

OTHER CROPS

Peas and Beans
Peas and beans are the most concentrated protein foods that can be grown. Unfortunately, over the years the general lack of yield has led to little interest being shown in this type of crop. Traditionally, a mixture of pulse crops were grown with cereals but this practice has virtually ceased. Straight cereals can be supplemented with protein as required, it will also be easier to find alternative uses for a crop if it is grown singly, and this may make the disposal of surpluses simpler.

Root Crops for Cows (*Mangold Turnips, Swedes, Fodder Beet*)
The area of root crops grown for cows has considerably declined, largely due to the high labour requirement for the crop. Mechanisation of precision drilling, pre-emergence sprays and harvesting now allow the crop to be considered for use on a dairy farm. The husbandry requirements are a good seed bed, early sowing, together with a reasonable level of manure and fertiliser application. For example, fodder beet and mangolds should get as a minimum, per hectare, 24 tonne dung and/or up to 600 kg/hectare of 10 per cent N, 25 per cent P_2O_5, 15 per cent K_2O.

Roots have a liking for humus and whatever dung or slurry can be applied before ploughing will always be well utilised.

Choose high dry-matter varieties of fodder beet and mangolds, sow before May if soil and weather conditions permit; single when the plant is small. With fodder beet use easily lifted varieties; mechanical harvesters are now widely available.

Turnips and swedes are susceptible to attack by turnip flea beetle; control is possible by seed dressing or low-volume sprays. Preventative methods should be applied when the seedlings are about to emerge (i.e. seven to ten days after sowing).

Turnips and swedes are more generally grown in the West and North of England, Scotland and Northern Ireland, rather than the lower rainfall areas of the East and South-East. If the crop is to be considered, it should only be grown with the full use of precision drilling and pre-emergence spraying for weed control.

Because turnips are particularly susceptible to frost the dairy farmer should grow only as much as can be consumed on, or soon after, lifting. Mangolds are not frost resistant and are generally lifted and stored in the autumn for use after Christmas. The leaves can be left on if haulage distance is short but otherwise are best removed as they have no feeding value. Mangolds can be stored in a building with suitable precautions against frost, such as insu-

Above: This vacuum-filled tanker has a compressed air discharge. Distribution is by jetting against a deflector plate to form a fan spray, but it needs dry land for winter application.

Left: 270 litres of material a minute can be discharged through this manure gun, which has a throw of 27 m. Care is necessary during winter to prevent freezing of pipes. If used when the ground is frozen, there is also the risk of direct run-off into a watercourse.

Below: This central double-sided bulk-feeding system is served either by tower silos or direct by self-unloading trailers for summertime zero grazing. The feed bunks are protected by a 'grille' of electric fencing wires against over-eager cows and are filled by chain and flight conveyor.

Above: A portable concrete feeding trough.

Right: An auger-feeding installation on a Cumberland farm.

Friesians strip-grazing four-year-old tetraploid ryegrass ley on a Norfolk farm.

The last part of the access corridor to these paddocks used to get very muddy in wet weather; so its width was halved to 4·5 m and the corridor concreted.

Where kale follows grass, a new technique that involves spraying the grass with paraquat and drilling direct into the killed sward saves cultivation cost and reduces poaching in winter.

Control of fat hen in kale; the plants on the left were sprayed with weedkiller, those on the right unsprayed.

Three methods of bale handling

Left: Handling bales with a fore loader.

Centre: Known as the 'bale squeezer', this implement handles 40 bales at a time; all the controls are hydraulic.

Below: 'Big bale' handling with a Howard baler.

lation with straw bales. Digestive and scouring troubles arise if mangolds are fed before being allowed to mature in the clamp. Swedes can be left longer in the ground, having considerable powers of resistance to frost. They are usually fed following turnips, when they have been used up from the New Year onwards.

Fodder beet with a higher dry matter did have a spell of popularity in the mid-fifties and seems to be creating interest currently as a farm-produced source of energy. Fodder beet and sugar beet tops are a most useful autumn supplement to the grazing, but must be fed clean and wilted. They should be introduced slowly into the diet and not fed beyond a level of 3·6–4·5 kg per 100 kg live weight.

Spreading the tops on a clean grass field and folding off behind an electric fence is a good way of controlling consumption and at the same time avoiding the digestive troubles so often prevalent when soiled tops are consumed ad lib. An additional safeguard against this trouble is to ensure that the tops are wilted; should they be fed fresh sprinkle with chalk at the rate of 112–168 g per 100 kg.

Arable Silage
Arable silage is a useful home-grown fodder crop. Traditionally it consisted of a mixture of cereals and pulses; research indicated that heavier yields were to be obtained from the pure cereal crops. The crop can be either autumn- or spring-sown. Both the seed rate and fertiliser dressing would be 150 per cent the rate of a normal cereal crop.

The objective would be to cut a heavy yield of reasonable quality fodder of 35–40 tonne per hectare.

For optimal feed value and bulk the crop should be cut just before the ear is shot. An arable silage crop will make a good nurse crop for maiden seeds and shares the heavy overhead cost of direct reseeding. In other situations it could be followed by other catch crops. Arable silage does not have enough feed value for high-yielding dairy cows but can be used as a supplier of adequate bulk to see the winter through; also it is very useful for young stock feeding.

Maize
Maize has become a popular crop on the dairy farm during the seventies particularly because of its ability to make good use of slurry as a fertiliser. Maize is susceptible to frost so drilling must be delayed until mid-April or early to mid-May. In the North of

England maize seed will only germinate when there is a soil temperature of 10°C at 10 cm.

Seed rate is 34–39 kg/hectare in 76 cm drills for mechanical harvesting. Apply fertiliser in the seed bed in the rate of 125 kg N, 60 kg P, 60 kg K per hectare. Protect the crop from birds with black cotton or bird scarers until 23–25 cm tall. Weed control is an important part of the husbandry and use is recommended of pre- and post-emergence sprays (paraquat at 2·8 litres/hectare and atrazine at 2·2–3·4 kg/hectare).

The NIAB Farmers' Leaflet lists the range of forage maize available, e.g. LG11, INRA240, Fronica and Caldera 535.

Harvesting will take place in late September–early October to give the maximum yield of good-quality silage after a growing period of about 150 days. Yields are of the order of 37–42 tonne per hectare.

Cabbages and Kale

Cabbages do provide a good feed for dairy cows; however, in recent years they have fallen out of favour due to the high labour requirement.

Kale is still a very popular crop and lends itself to the increasing use of machinery, both in growing and harvesting the crop. Kale can be drilled at 4·5 kg per hectare in rows 69 cm apart. The seed is more often broadcast. The crop is very responsive to fertilisers and will give a good return to 600 kg per hectare of 20:10:10 fertiliser. In the seed bed, a further top dressing of 100 kg of nitrogen will ensure a good yield.

These levels can be reduced if a good dressing of dung (50–63 tonne per hectare) is applied. Yields of 20–35 tonne per hectare are possible. Kale can be usefully grazed in autumn and then zero-grazed into mid-winter.

The varieties of kale have differing degrees of resistance to frost. Popular varieties of kale include Canson, Thousand Head, Marrow Stem, Gigantic, Maris Kestrel.

Feeding frosted kale to cattle causes digestive upsets and causes milk yields to drop alarmingly. One of the problems of grazing kale is the shorting of the electric fencing wire.

FORAGE FARMING

The name describes the system whereby maximum use is made of forage crops which are grazed in situ. This reduces the amount of handling and hence heavy labour costs. The harvesting of forage crops now has been mechanised and is commonly described as zero-grazing; it is used extensively in the autumn and spring periods. This overcomes the problems of cattle expending much energy when going out to graze the forage crop.

Forage crops are very suitable for feeding to cows in mid and late lactation and also for dry cows. Cows in early lactation need less forage and the diet must be much higher in energy.

When forage crops are used either grazed or in situ, it is very important to regulate the supply of the crop to the cow. This is particularly important in the spring.

In many cases when a dairy herd is put on to supplementary forage feeding, not enough thought is given to the availability of 'follow-on crops'. Much use is then to be made of the forage crops as a means of changing from full winter rations to spring grazing.

The forage should allow the same level of milk from bulk feeds to be continued; to ask for increased milk from forage at this time is unwise. Winter rye is a leafy succulent crop which has often been exploited too far.

Table 6.2. Sequence of Forage Crops

Period of use	Crop	Date of sowing
March/April	Rye/Italian ryegrass	Early Autumn
July/August	Arable silage aftermath	Autumn or spring
August/November	Fodder maize	May
Sept./December	Italian ryegrass/trefoil	Spring (under corn)
	Marrow stem kale	Spring
Sept./December	Fodder turnips	July and August
January/March	Thousand head kale	Late spring
	Hungry gap kale	Late summer

Seeding rates for these crops and expected yields at time of grazing:

Crop	Seed rate per hectare	Yield per hectare (dependent upon stage of growth)
Italian ryegrass	22 kg Ryegrass	10–20 tonnes
Rye	125 kg Rye	10–20 tonnes
Rape	6–7 kg	15–20 tonnes
Italian ryegrass /trefoil	Italian 9·0 kg / Trefoil 6·7 kg	10 tonnes
Marrow stem kale	6·7 kg (broadcast)	30 tonnes
Thousand head kale	4·5 kg (drilled)	25 tonnes
Hungry gap kale		15 tonnes

After grass a new technique involving spraying turf with paraquat and then direct drilling saves cultivation cost and reduces poaching in winter. These crops will give grazing at times of the year when grass is dormant in the early spring or is making little growth as a result of drought. All respond to generous applications of nitrogen. Most of these crops can be grown as catch crops, thus increasing production over the rotation without diminishing the area of land devoted to cash crops—which arable/dairy farmers would be loath to do.

The use of forage crops can undoubtedly help to increase output per hectare on dairy farms and reduce feeding costs. The system allows wide scope for originality and initiative in the cropping rotation.

One further advantage of growing forage crops on the mainly grass farm is that land ploughed could be well dressed with dung or slurry prior to ploughing. Where to apply dung or slurry with the increasing size of dairy herds has become quite a problem on mainly grass farms.

CHAPTER 7

THE CHEAPEST FOOD FOR MILK

TEMPORARY and permanent pastures occupy 7·0 million hectares compared with an arable area of 5·0 million hectares in Great Britain as a whole. It has been estimated that this area of grass supplies around 45 per cent of the total energy consumed by livestock in this country, though occupying some 60 per cent of the total agricultural land. It follows, therefore, that production per hectare of grass is appreciably lower than production per hectare of arable—a significant fact in the economy of this country at the present time. Yet, to dairy farmers, grass represents his main and often sole source of nutrients for the dairy cow during at least four months of the year, and is undoubtedly the cheapest source of nutrients consumed by the grazing animal.

Further, as shown in Chapter 5, conserved grass in the form of hay and silage are two of the cheapest sources of starch and protein available for winter feeding. Thus grassland should be able to make a greatly increased contribution to the economics of dairy farming generally.

INCREASING PRODUCTION FROM GRASS

To achieve this, there are three lines of attack for dairy farmers to consider. First, increased yield of grass per hectare by better establishment, better management of established leys and permanent grass and a higher level of fertiliser treatment.

For a discussion on pasture establishment and seeds mixture, the reader should refer to books on grassland husbandry, but, in general dairy farm management, the concept of grass as a crop entitled to proper fertiliser treatment and to adequate periods of rest followed by defoliation—grazing or mowing—would help to establish grassland management on a higher level.

Many pastures are seriously reduced in productivity by over-grazing and treading in the winter and by under-grazing in the summer.

Secondly, excess grass should be properly conserved during its peak periods of production, May–June, and again in September, when growth is out of proportion to the stock carried.

These peak surpluses are normally conserved in the form of hay, silage or dried grass, and the merits of the different methods are considered later.

Thirdly, there should be better utilisation by the grazing animal. This involves heavier stocking and improved grazing techniques to reduce waste in consumption and by limiting the intake of grass to give more efficient digestion of what is eaten. This aspect of rationing the cow's feeding—particularly concerned with grass—is dealt with fully in Chapter 11.

The Place for Hay

As a means of raising output per hectare, haymaking compares unfavourably with silage-making or grass-drying. It represents an extensive rather than an intensive method of land use and is therefore more fitted to large-scale farming that to the smaller and more intensely managed farms.

Haymaking has been improved and made more efficient by the introduction of mechanisation, thus improving output per man considerably, particularly in favourable weather. Hay as a feedstuff is easily fed and can be rationed accurately. Its quality can be extremely variable, from a value no better than cereal straw to a feed of the value of bran. This variation depends on stage of growth in the grass at cutting; the earlier the hay is cut once the flowering head is formed, the higher its feeding value, provided weathering loss is reduced to a minimum.

The weather hazard is the big difficulty in haymaking. Traditionally, hay was left to mature in the field. The modern trend is to work the hay intensively after cutting. This, coupled with the appropriate weather, can ensure a good product.

The essential points in conserving are:

● cut early in the season
● only cut an area that can be easily handled, taking into account the current weather
● in good weather, work the cut grass to 'make' the hay suitable for baling
● minimise the time it is left out on the field.

Risks with Baling
For larger farms, the choice of haymaking equipment largely depends on the area to be handled and the capital available.

Desirable as high labour output per man is, its pursuit in hay-making is often attended by reduced feeding value in the product, as compared with the quality achieved by more laborious hand methods. For example, the great danger in baling is mouldiness in the bales through bale hay which is still damp. Hay for baling must be thoroughly dry right through the swath; tedding is rec-ommended in addition to swath turning. Forage harvesters have been adapted to operate at lower rotor speeds for crushing hay and facilitating drying in the swath. Roller or crimping machines are now available for the same purpose.

In favourable weather hay so treated can be baled within forty-eight hours of cutting. Do not bale until the dew has com-pletely lifted in the morning and before it comes down in the evening. Give the bales time to 'sweat' in the field; small bales should be set up in the field if rain threatens. Barn hay-drying does offer some solution to risk of exposure to weather.

Density of Bale and Moisture Content
If the moisture content of the hay is high—then bale loosely. Cashmore gives the formula:

$$D = 30 - \tfrac{2}{3}M \text{ when: } D = \text{bale density kg per m}^3$$
$$M = \text{moisture content.}$$

Thus at a moisture content of 24 per cent, when hay is just fit to stack, the bale density is 244 kg per m^3, whereas at 18 per cent moisture, i.e. very dry, the density can be 288 kg per m^3. Most bales are 0·14 m^3.

Where hay is made in the stack, heating and mould formation must be avoided, otherwise there will be considerable loss of feeding value and reduced palatability. Heating is avoided by having the hay sufficiently free from sap before stacking; moul-diness is prevented by having the hay protected from dew or rain when gathered and preventing damp from entering the stack. Mouldiness is in the upper layer of a bale stack and is less likely to develop if the stack is covered by a layer of loose straw to the depth of about one-third metre.

The weather hazards associated with haymaking can be min-imised by use of the Farmers' Weather Service, available at the Meteorological Office at Bracknell. Notice of dry-weather periods can be obtained.

Feeding Value of Hay

The quality of hay is very variable, as already described, depending on the time of cutting and degree of weathering. The feed values range as shown in Table 7.1.

Table 7.1. Feeding Value of Hay

Type of hay	DM per cent	ME MJ/kg	DCP per cent	D value	Fibre
Very high digestibility	85	10·1	9·0	67	29·1
Moderate digestibility	85	8·4	3·9	57	32·8
Very low digestibility	85	7·5	3·8	47	34·0

(*Nutrient Allowances and Composition of Feeding Stuffs for Ruminants*, MAFF.)

The very best hay has an energy value that is comparable to good silage. If all hay was well made at the right time, then hay would be a valuable food. Hay well made from grass cut at the flowering stage will provide for maintenance and production of up to nine litres of milk per cow per day, if fed to appetite level; whereas poor-quality hay—even when fed to the same level—will do no more than satisfy the maintenance requirement.

SILAGE MAKING

Compared with haymaking, silage making offers a means of conserving grass at an earlier and more nutritive stage of growth, without the weather risk of the former process. The technique involved in making good silage is now more widely understood, and, as a conservation process, silage making has made great strides in recent years.

Provided grassland is managed properly and adequately fertilised, silage making can begin two to four weeks before the normal time for haymaking. This is the first step in making better use of the grass crop.

There has been considerable progress in the mechanisation of the silage-making process. The forage harvester has developed from single to double and eventually to precision chop. The size of trailers has been increased up to 6 tonne capacity. The process of wilting was introduced by the mid-sixties, which superseded the previous direct cut system.

Attention was directed towards making high dry-matter silages (25–30 per cent DM); this made the grass cutting an operation additional to the actual grass pick-up. Where grass was stored in towers, dry matter of 30 per cent plus was looked for. However, on the average farm with clamp silages the desired matter is recommended to be in the 25–30 per cent range.

Silage effluent has become a serious problem, being highly pollutant. A small quantity has a disastrous effect on aquatic life in watercourses. It should be collected in a sealed tank allowing 23 litres of capacity per tonne of material ensiled. Where herbage dry matter is below 20 per cent the dry-matter loss in effluent can be as high as 20 per cent; with herbage dry-matter content exceeding 25 per cent, there is no effluent problem.

On clamp silages, the buckrake is used to place the grass in the clamp, after being ferried from the field by the tipping trailers.

The development of self-feed silage eliminates the problem of handling silage a second time out of the clamp. The self-feed system does provide a constraint to the number of cows which can be fed on the self-feed silage face. In the early seventies as size of herd increased many farmers moved to 'easy-feed' silage. This involves providing a feed fence where the silage can be placed each day.

The easy-fed system allows a check to be made on the amount of silage fed to the cows. A wide range of equipment is available such as forage boxes, fore-end loaders and block cutters which greatly reduce the labour requirements. However, these systems require more capital and must not be embarked upon lightly.

The weight of silage removed from the clamp is at least 25–33 per cent less than the grass ensiled. This can be attributed to effluent and the respiration losses, which in turn encourage the desirable lactic acid fermentation process. Further losses due to weathering and deterioration of the outside layers of silage are minimised by proper and thorough consolidation and protection with a covering plastic sheet to reduce seepage of rain into the clamp. It is desirable to have silage clamps covered but this involves considerable capital expense, and is difficult to justify.

Points to Watch
Much effort is put into the provision of good grass for silage making, but this effort can be wasted through poor techniques of filling and sealing. Unfortunately, most of the wastages occur inside

Using a front-end fore-loader
for making clamp silage.

Unloading at the clamp from
a muck spreader fitted with
silage sides.

Here a blower is being used to fill a self-feed silage clamp with precision chopped material dropped into a moving bed dump box.

A forage box and grain blower filling a bunker silo. The material being sprayed in requires little additional compaction, thus saving labour, improving fermentation, and resulting in a friable product that is easy to extract.

Harvesting oats with a self-propelled direct-cut forage harvester at Harper Adams Agricultural College. The crop was then stored in a tower silo and fed to the dairy herd. An advantage of whole-crop silage is that, given reasonable weather conditions, a very uniform product can be stored, whereas with grass silage it is rare to achieve uniformity throughout the whole of the clamp and from season to season.

Barn hay-drying. The advantages of this method of reducing the moisture content include improved yield of dry-matter per hectare and the greater feeding value. However, it has been slow to develop and perhaps less than 4 per cent of the hay in the UK is made this way.

the pit so it goes on unseen. This makes it so important, for the basic rules of good silage making must be adhered to. The following are the important points to remember in making silage.

1. The wilted grass must be distributed evenly throughout the clamp. Avoid pockets of air and achieve good consolidation. These are the first steps to control the initial temperature which in turn controls the initial period of aerobic fermentation. Temperatures above 32°C lead to the development of moulds. Higher temperatures are a direct result of an unrestricted respiration process which of course burns off much of the available carbohydrates and renders the protein indigestible.

2. The best way to contain the temperature and excessive fermentation losses is to prevent air getting into the pit. The practical way to achieve this is to cover the pit with plastic sheets every night. This is a discipline which must be operated on every silage pit.

3. Losses in the pit are aggravated by slow filling and by large pits with large surface areas. The most effective way of limiting these features is to use the Dorset Wedge system of filling the pit. The technique is to fill the material into the pit in a wedge shape, starting at the back wall of the pit. As the grass comes in so the pit fills and the front of the wedge is maintained as a steep ramp. The grass filled in to the appropriate height is sheeted down progressively as the ramp moves forward. The sheet can be secured by straw bales or old tyres. Final sealing should take place as soon as filling has been completed.

4. Care should be taken to eliminate wastage on the shoulder, i.e. the join between the silage and the pit wall. The walls ideally should be sealed to prevent ingress of air, and plastic sheets used for this purpose can be folded under the top sheet to give an airtight seal.

5. Problems arise with grass coming into the pit which is either too dry or too wet. Excessively wilted grass will tend to overheat in the pit; extra consolidation will have to be provided. Highly wilted grass, of course, suffers from excessive field losses as well. Grass which is put into the pit with too much moisture requires little consolidation. It quickly settles, drives out the air, prevents heating and an inevitable end product is cold butyric acid silage, an anaerobic process which not only consumes sugars but allows protein breakdown, resulting in a foul-smelling product which is

unpalatable to stock. As mentioned previously, a 25–30 per cent dry-matter grass is likely to make the best type of silage.

Additives in Silage Making

The objective in the silage-making process is to preserve grass at its best nutritive level. This is achieved by encouraging the desirable lactic acid fermentation process to produce a pH of about 4·3–4·5 which will inhibit mould and putrefactive bacteria. The desired level of acidity, $2\frac{1}{2}$ per cent lactic acid concentration, will ensure a state of stability in the silage pit.

Additives have been developed and used to achieve this stability more quickly. Molasses has been used for some time as a means of supplying a supplement to plant sugars, which could be readily converted into lactic acid.

In Finland, the AIV process provided mineral acids to halt growth of all bacteria and moulds, but it was necessary to neutralise the acids before feeding.

There is a quite a range of additives available in the United Kingdom. The general aim is to supplement the natural fermentation process either by providing readily fermentable material or supplying acid which will more quickly provide a pH level in the silage to check the fermentation process.

The main mineral acids used are formic and sulphuric. Formalin is also used as a preservative in some cases. It is most important to read the instruction notes as to the use of concentration of additives and the provision of protective clothing.

Widespread field trials indicate that additives do help to provide a better-quality silage product which is then capable of providing a better cash return to the dairy herd.

Quality and Quantity

There is a very close relationship between the yield of grass per cut and the quality of the ensuing silage. For many years some farmers have thought of silage almost as a salvage operation, after constant rain has ruined the haymaking schedule. Modern thinking is concerned with attempting to obtain as much good quality silage as possible. Multi-cut silage, a system of taking at least four cuts during the season, was evolved during the mid-seventies. Unfortunately, such a system cannot cope with a succession of dry summers and subsequently lost favour.

A more traditional three cuts are taken on most silage farms.

Table 7.2 illustrates the range of feed values possible and emphasises the importance of good grass being made into good silage. Skilled silage makers often attain levels up to 11 MJ/kg, which is obviously a highly prized feed level.

On mainly grass farms in the West it should be possible to harvest about 49 tonne of wet grass per hectare (3 cuts), giving a possible 7 tonne per cow which would suffice for a full winter (180 days) on a ration of silage (self-feed) and concentrates.

Table 7.2. Average Values of Silage

	DM	ME MJ/kg	DCP per cent	D value
Grass—Very high D	25	10·2	11·6	67
high D	25	9·3	10·7	61
moderate D	25	8·8	10·2	58
low D	25	7·6	9·8	52

(*Nutrient Allowances and Composition of Feeding Stuffs for Ruminants*, MAFF.)

In a dry season, if it seems likely that the required silage tonnage is not going to be available, then steps should be taken by mid-summer to supplement the silage by purchased feeds, e.g. hay, brewers' grains, or sugar beet pulp.

In the economy of crop production on dairy farms today, silage making must play an ever-increasing role. Efforts must be made to make as much silage as possible from grass in the spring. When there is a flush of grass in September, this can be cut for silage, and used satisfactorily for dairy followers. Silage, if adequately sheeted down and protected, can be stored over to the following winter. It would always be a useful supplement in a very dry summer.

An interesting recent development has been the introduction of Big Bale Silage. This has tended to be of interest on the Eastern areas of the country where big balers are already available and can be used for this technique. The capital cost is minimal compared to the more traditional silage making methods. It will be interesting to follow this development; as yet, more work needs to be done before the system can be fully evaluated.

Ensiling Brewers' Grains
If, as has been previously suggested, the silage availability is less than that required, a very suitable supplement can be provided in brewers' grains. Deliveries can be arranged on a regular basis

throughout the winter, but a better way to secure the supply is to have them delivered during the summer months, and to ensile them. The grains can be put under grass silage, to be delivered before the first grass cut is made. Alternatively, grains can be stored in any form of airtight silo, be it concrete or the temporary wire-mesh cylindrical silo.

One tonne of wet grains will occupy $1.9\,m^3$. The silo should be well consolidated and sealed immediately after filling. Grains can be stored successfully in a variety of buildings, such as Dutch barns lined with sleepers. Brewers' grains exert considerable lateral pressure, depth for depth greater than grass silage, and can be dangerous. Advice on new buildings and conversion of existing buildings can be obtained from the local ADAS adviser.

Brewers' grains have a feeding value equivalent to good silage on a DM basis. (DM—28 per cent, ME—$10.0\,MJ/kg$, DCP—14.9 per cent)

Maize Silage
Modern forage harvesters fitted with the suitable maize attachment can handle the average maize crops quite successfully. Maize silage is easy to make provided it is well chopped (preferably precision chopped), the silo filled rapidly, and sealed as soon as possible after filling. Maize silage is highly palatable but of a low protein content—typical analysis would be DM—21 per cent, ME—10.8 MJ/kg, DCP—7 per cent with D value of 65. The digestibility of the maize crop is high and changes little during the later stages of growth. It is a high-energy type of silage which, if used for milking cows, needs supplementing with protein. Experience suggests that it is best fed in conjunction with grass silage at a 60 per cent grass–40 per cent maize silage ratio. Maize silage is very suitable for feeding to beef cattle and young stock.

GRASS DRYING

As a conservation process, grass drying is the one accompanied by least loss between the field and the cow and, as with silage making, is to a large extent free of weather risks.

When grass is artificially dried, it can be cut and conserved in the very early stages of growth when it is 10 to 15 cm long and at its highest feeding value.

The disadvantages of the process are the capital costs of the equipment and the fuel involved. Because of these high capital overheads, grass drying must be associated with a high throughput and a long drying season to be economically viable.

Manuring, cutting and wilting have all to be closely integrated to ensure an adequate supply of the correct type of grass to the drier.

With the escalation of fuel costs, dried grass is no longer able to compete as a bulk fodder food, but must be considered as a cheaper home-grown concentrate, comparable in price to barley and sugar beet nuts. Dried grass is now almost wholly produced as a commercial product; few, if any, farmers can contemplate grass drying on a farm scale for home consumption.

Barn Hay Drying

There are several types of barn hay-drying units. It is essentially a high-volume fan driven by a diesel engine or tractor. The air is driven through the stack of bales either through centrally positioned tunnels or a central vertical shaft. Bales are to be placed such that the air must pass through them. The system can produce good quality hay but involves quite a lot of handling. Consequently it is only likely to be applicable on a farm with a small herd of about sixty cows or less.

HAYLAGE

Haylage is a sweet-smelling fodder produced by wilting grass to 40–60 per cent moisture in the field. The time taken to achieve this is variable, depending upon weather and amount of 'working'. The wilted grass is then picked up with a meter chop forage harvester and transported in self-unloading trailers. These deliver the grass into a forage blower which then conveys it into an airtight tower silo.

Preservation of the wilted grass is ensured by the presence of carbon dioxide—a respiration by-product.

The concrete or steel-sheeted towers have mechanical unloaders and discharge into forage boxes or automatic auger conveyors into adjoining stockyards.

Labour costs are minimised and the system is suited to a controlled feeding policy. It does fit in very well with the yard and parlour system.

FOUR PRINCIPLES

Indeed, the vital role that grassland can play generally in cheapening the cost of milk production makes it imperative for every farmer to make a definite plan of action covering every facet of his grassland management. He should:

1. Treat grass as a definite crop, with periods of rest and production, avoiding heavy winter grazing.

2. Increase production by adequate liming, manuring and surface cultivation and resolve that the poorest fields will be improved by eventual ploughing out and reseeding to grass as circumstances allow.

3. Plan for the extension of the grazing seasons, by the provision of an early bite and autumn grazing—particularly from maiden seeds.

4. Employ better methods of utilisation through controlled grazing (see Chapter 11) and better methods of conservation—as described here—whether for silage, hay or dried grass.

GRASSLAND RECORDING

Many farmers grow grass but few consider it necessary to record production from grass. The recording of grassland comes into two categories:

● the effective use of grass on a day to day basis, using a net output method;
● the recording of grassland use over a whole season; thus allowing a comparison of husbandry systems, levels and timing of fertiliser applications etc.

These systems can be illustrated as follows:

1. Day-to-day Grass Use. Once the grass is grown, the most important feature is to make best use of it. A fairly simple means of assessing grass use as a means of producing milk is to compare the output of milk with the input of supplementary over a period of time—one week is suggested. This will tend to even out daily fluctuations, so that for a 120-cow herd, largely autumn calving out to grass in mid-July, the results might be as shown in Table 7.3.

The grass at this time was providing for Maintenance (M) + 9·4 litres milk per cow. This was a herd level of production. It must be realised that within the herd, late autumn calvers are producing 12 litres from grass whereas spring calvers would only be taking 5–7·5 litres per day from grass.

The level of concentrate usage at 0·19 kg/litre and milk produced per cow are indicative of the herd production at this time of year. If this kind of assessment is carried out on a regular weekly basis the pattern of production throughout the year can be established.

Table 7.3

Total milk from the herd (76 cows in milk):	9711 litres
Total concentrates for the week:	1875 kg
(using medium-energy concentrates at 0·4 kg per litre)	
Milk produced from concentrates:	$\dfrac{1875}{0\cdot4} = 4687\cdot5$ litres

Milk from grassland	
Total milk:	9711 litres
less milk from concentrates:	4687 litres
equals:	5024 litres
Milk from grass per cow per day:	$\dfrac{5024}{\text{No. of cows in milk (76)} \times 7} = 9\cdot4$ litres
Milk produced per cow per day:	$\dfrac{9711}{532} = 18\cdot2$ litres
Concentrate usage (kg/litre):	$\dfrac{1875}{9711} = 0\cdot19$ kg/litre

2. The system suggested by the British Grassland Society is based on the number of cow days recorded per hectare; a cow day represents the amount of bulk food consumed in twenty-four hours by the average lactating cow. Adjustment is made to the total of grazing cow days for any supplementary food fed or grass conserved as hay or silage, as shown in Table 7.4.

Table 7.4. Cow Days per Tonne of Feed (either fed or conserved)

	Friesian Shorthorn	Ayrshire	Guernsey	Jersey
Hay	68	80	97	112
Silage 20 per cent DM	21	25	30	32
Kale	17	19	22	25
Brewers' grains (wet)	26	32	37	45
	Adjustment for concentrate feeding			
Cow days to be subtracted per 50 kg fed	2·4	2·9	3·4	3·9

Information on grassland recording can be obtained from the Secretary of the British Grassland Society, Grassland Research Institute, Hurley, Berkshire.

CHAPTER 8

SCIENTIFIC BASIS FOR COW FEEDING

CAREFULLY controlled feeding experiments have enabled scientists to state the requirements of farm animals in two definite terms:

1. The maintenance requirement which can be defined as that portion of the food eaten which is used to sustain life and health without loss of body weight. This is, of course, the priority requirement with all classes of stock.

2. The production requirement which relates to the food needs for:

● increase in liveweight—either as growth in young animals or increasing bodily condition in mature animals;
● the production of milk in the lactating cow, sow, mare or ewe;
● the performance of work in the case of a horse or other beast of burden.

It follows therefore that only when the rations fed to farm stock exceed maintenance requirements can any form of production as meat, milk, wool or work be expected.

The method of expressing food requirements has been the subject of much discussion and thought in the United Kingdom for many years. In 1975 a joint working party of researchers, advisers and teachers produced a report, *Energy Allowances and Feeding Systems for Ruminants*—Ministry of Agriculture Technical Bulletin No. 33, which was adopted in the United Kingdom, replacing the previous Starch Equivalent System. The new system was concerned with the use of Metabolisable Energy as a basis for formulating rations on the farm.

THE DAIRY COW and the ME SYSTEM

The basal unit of energy in the ME system is the megajoule (MJ). All foods contain energy, but it is not all available to the animal. Part of the energy is lost in the animal faeces, i.e. that part of the food described as indigestible. Other losses of energy occur in the production of gas, methane, the urine of the animal, and the loss of body heat. The energy remaining is referred to as 'metabolisable'.

The basis of any rationing system is the matching up of the energy requirements of the animal to that which is available in the ration supplied.

The requirements of metabolisable energy for maintenance and production are supplied in Table 8.1.

Table 8.1. Maintenance Requirement per Day of Metabolisable Energy and Digestible Crude Protein DCP

Breed type	Liveweight (kg)	Maintenance requirement ME MJ/day	DCP g/day	Hay kg
S. Devon	650	67	365	10
Friesians	600	63	345	9·5
Shorthorn	550	59	325	9
Ayrshire	500	54	300	8·5
Guernsey	450	49	275	8
Jersey	400	45	250	7·5

(*Nutrient Allowances and Composition of Feedingstuffs for Nutrients*, MAFF.)

Table 8.2. Production Requirements per Kilogram of Milk of Varying Compositional Quality

Quality of milk bf	snf	Breed type	ME MJ/kg	DCP g/kg
4·9	9·1	Channel Island	6·0	63
3·8	8·7	Ayrshire	5·1	53
3·6	8·6	Friesian	4·9	48

(*Energy Allowances and Feeding Systems for Ruminants*, (MAFF.))

One of the factors that was not previously considered in rationing dairy cows was the loss and gain of liveweight through the lactation. This has been taken care of by the ME system. For 1 kg of liveweight loss there is a contribution of 28 MJ of dietary ME, and for a gain of 1 kg of liveweight, the ration must supply an extra allowance of 34 MJ.

There is a range of energy and protein allowances between and even within breeds. Generally speaking, better feeding allows dairy cows to attain their genetic potential in terms of quality, and this aspect is becoming increasingly important as payment depends increasingly on quality.

Table 8.3. Possible Dry-Matter Intakes of Dairy Cows at Different Milk Levels

| | Milk yield kg/day | | | | | |
Liveweight	5	10	15	20	25	30
650	16·8	17·3	17·8	18·3	18·8	19·3
600	15·5	16·0	16·5	17·0	17·5	18·0
550	14·3	14·8	15·3	15·8	16·3	16·8
500	13·0	13·5	14·0	14·5	15·0	15·5
450	11·8	12·3	12·8	13·3	13·8	14·3
400	10·5	11·0	11·5	12·0	12·5	13·0

(*Energy Allowances and Feeding Systems for Ruminants*, MAFF.)

In early lactation due to stress of calving, the appetite is known to be reduced by probably 2–3 kg per day, less than the normally expected intake. Once the energy, protein and dry matter intake of the animal are known, the next step is to assess the foodstuffs available on the farm and match the food available to the input levels required.

DRY MATTER INTAKE

Having calculated the ME and DCP requirements of a cow, the last basic consideration to take into account is the amount of food that an animal will eat. This could be difficult when one takes account of the varying dry matter of different types of foods. However, the calculations are simplified by having all food intakes related to the dry matter intake of the cow. Table 8.4 shows how

Table 8.4. Example of DM, ME and DCP requirements for a Friesian cow of 550 kg weight

The cow is in mid-lactation, giving 20 kg milk and requiring to put on 0·5 kg/day liveweight gain.

Foods available:
Silage: DM—25%, ME—10 MJ/kg DM, DCP—116 g/kg DM
Sugar Beet Nuts: DM—90%, ME—12·7 MJ/kg DM, DCP—59 kg DM
Concentrates: DM—85%, ME—12·5 MJ/kg DM, DCP—112 g/kg DM.

Requirements	DM kg	ME MJ/kg DM	DCP g/kg DM
Dry Matter Intake	15·8	—	—
Maintenance 550 kg	—	59	310
Production: 20 kg @ 4·9 MJ/litre	—	98	960
Liveweight gain 0·5 kg/day @ 34 MJ/kg	—	17	—
TOTAL	15·8	174	1270
A possible ration would be:			
30 kg silage	7·5	75	870
1·5 kg sugar beet pulp nuts	1·35	17·1	79·6
	8·85	92·1	949·6
To be supplied by the production rations:	6·95	81·9	320·4
8·1 kg concentrates would provide:	6·95	86·8	778·4
Discrepancy	—	4·9	458

In this case the ration satisfies the dry matter and ME requirements of the cow. There would appear to be an excess of DCP which is likely to happen where silage is the bulk food used. There has been much discussion in recent years concerning the process whereby some protein can be digested in the rumen while the undigested portion passes through to the true stomach of the cow. A joint working party is currently researching the protein story and a report is expected to be available during the next few years.

Generally speaking from a practical point of view, higher levels of protein are certainly needed for the higher levels of milk production, i.e. in the order of 30–40 litres or more.

the cow's appetite in terms of dry matter intake per day is related to bodyweight and also to the amount of milk being given.

In the case of high-yielding cows, it is a fact that in practice, such cows often have the ability to eat far more than the theoretical amounts of dry matter.

SCIENCE INTO PRACTICE

The feeding standards illustrate the variations in the food requirements of dairy cows both in respect of the breed and the quality of the milk produced. To use them in practice it must be remembered that dry matter intake by the cow is governed by appetite and the palatability of the foods fed. Mention has been made of the varying moisture contents of feeds. In practice, there are many simple features which have to be borne in mind when making up rations. Sugar beet pulp, for example, swells when moistened and gives the cow a feeling of repletion actually before the required dry matter intake has been consumed. Furthermore, food intake per day is dependent on the speed at which it passes through the cow and is digested. On a laxative diet, possibly spring grass, as the food is low in fibre it passes through the animal so quickly that the animal cannot extract enough energy to satisfy its needs. On a high-fibre diet, the throughput of food is much slower; the fibre is associated with nutrients being indigestible and once again the animal obtains less than her requirements of energy and protein.

A Silage Guide

Silage is a widely used food on dairy farms. The question of appetite and value of the ration becomes particularly important when deciding on the level of silage to be included on the diet. Silage is usually made in three cuts and there can be very different dry matters in each cut. As the cow progresses from one cut of silage to the next this change in dry matter content must be taken into account.

Table 8.5. A Guide to the Dry-Matter Content of Silage

Physical test	Percentage dry matter
Water easily squeezed out by hand	Under 18%
Water just expressed by hand	19–24%
Water not expressed by hand	Over 25%

In summary it can be said that the appetite of a cow is affected by:

● The production level and general rate of metabolism in the cow. High levels of production raise the appetite; ill health lowers it.
● Digestibility: foods of low digestibility depress the appetite.
● The size and relative digestive capacity (i.e. size of rumen) of the individual cow.

VALUE OF HOME-GROWN FOODS

With the knowledge of cows' food requirements, their digestive capacity and the feeding value of foods available, it is possible to feed along scientific and economic lines. The herdsman's real problem is determining the value of home-grown foods. Purchased feeding stuffs bought under guaranteed analyses as required under the Fertiliser and Feedingstuffs Act will vary very little in compositional quality. But this does not apply to home-grown feedstuffs which vary considerably in value and usually make up a major part of the cow's diet. It is vitally important, therefore, to be able to assess the feeding value of home-grown foods with reasonable accuracy.

The answer concerning the value of a diet must come inevitably from the cow herself. For years there has been too little correlation between the make-up of a ration and whether it achieved its desired objective. When a ration does not produce the desired result it is highly likely that the fault lies in the make-up of the ration and less likely that the cow is herself at fault. This emphasises the need to set up regular monitoring systems giving a detailed report of the relationships between milk output and feed input.

Know Stage of Growth

As has been pointed out in Chapter 7, the feeding value of grass and its conserved products varies with the stage of growth at which it is eaten or conserved. Increasing age, or decreasing rapidity of and a slowing down of the growth rate, are accompanied by a falling percentage of protein and a rising percentage of fibre. An increase in the amount of fibre consumed lowers the efficiency of digestion and forces a cow to work much harder in order to extract the available food nutrients.

This is of no great importance with low-yielding animals, but when high levels of production are the aim, the fibre intake becomes important.

Many of our home-produced foods are high in fibre. For example, most samples of hay will be within the range 25–35 per cent fibre with dried grass and silage varying from 20 to 30 per cent; whereas, in contrast, a typical compound cake or meal has from 8 to 10 per cent. It is essential, therefore, to know the stage of growth at which hay, silage or dried grass are cut. The earlier the cutting is taken, the lower is the fibre percentage.

More Fibre—Lower Value

Fibre is rather a loose term and difficult to define chemically. It comprises cellulose and hemi-cellulose, both readily digested unless

Urea-based supplements are available in liquid or solid form. The photo on the left shows a specially-designed feeder for the liquid supplement; the bottom picture shows an animal taking block supplement from a steel tub.

Getting an early bite from a ley top-dressed with nitrogen in February. To counteract the laxative nature of young grass and to mitigate the rick of bloat, the changeover from winter feed to summer grazing should be made gradually.

Grazing a ley during late summer. In practice, the production value of late season grass is at least 5 litres less per cow per day than similar grazing in spring.

tightly bonded to lignin (woody tissue) which in itself is non-digestible.

The make-up of the sward cut is important as certain grasses with a high stem-to-leaf ratio give rise to fibrous material. Loss of leaf in haymaking also results in a serious diminution of feeding value.

This lowering of feeding value with maturity is also seen in certain root crops such as marrow-stem kale which tends to lose its leaves and become increasingly fibrous after mid-winter. On the other hand, mangolds and swedes contain 12–18 per cent of fibre in the dry matter, so that they form excellent companion foods to feed with the fibrous cereal straws which contain from 30 to 40 per cent of fibre.

Basically, therefore, high-quality hay, silage or dried grass can only be made by conserving the right type of material at the right stage of growth.

A further factor of conservation is that of palatability. Well-made hay or silage is highly palatable. If hay is badly weathered or silage incorrectly fermented, both develop mould and there is a corresponding loss of feeding value and palatability. Less of the food is eaten, and more wasted.

Stockmen should also note that dirty feeding troughs, or soiling of the foods fed, for instance with earth or faeces—as often happens with sugar-beet tops—greatly reduces palatability.

Housing Affects Feeding

It must not be assumed, however, that the previous tables cover all the variations in maintenance and production requirements. In fact, they refer to a fairly standard set of conditions—namely those which occur when the cow is housed.

In practice, variations from these standards generally tend towards increasing maintenance requirements. Thus, when grazing, the cow uses up energy searching for her food, especially on thin, low-density swards or where long distances have to be travelled to water or pasture. And where cows are not housed, exposure to wet weather increases the heat loss from the body and raises the amount of maintenance food required.

No advantage is gained by keeping cows too warm: 10–13°C is about right. But cows should be able to lie down comfortably to rest and should not be forced to stand because of fear of aggressive companions in yards or adjoining stalls, or because of adverse conditions outdoors.

In regard to production requirements, it is not suggested that the above standards apply under all conditions. With high-yielding cows, or when feed prices are low relative to milk prices, it may well pay to feed slightly above the level of these feeding standards, but the increase in milk output for each increase in food consumed is subject to the law of diminishing returns which sets a ceiling on what is a profitable feeding level. In my opinion, even in times such as the present when feed costs are high, it is unwise to feed below the standard given.

LEARN FROM THE COWS

One last fact must be noted. Feeding standards must inevitably relate to the average cow but they may not fully meet the actual feed requirements or appetite of the individual cow.

In general, the higher the genetic milk potential of the cow, the greater is her digestive efficiency. If properly fed, she will produce milk more economically than the lower yielder, both in terms of energy and protein consumed. In most cases, she will also show a greater dry-matter consumption than the average cow, though 'shy feeders' with a high productive capacity are not uncommon.

Rigid adherence to feeding standards represent a pedantic approach to the problem. The wise and observant stockman is prepared to learn from his cows as to whether his theoretical estimation of their requirements is in fact producing the expected results. This can only be assessed if the quantities of food fed are known and there is a factual or objective appraisal of the cow's performance and condition.

WHEN COWS LOSE FLESH

Is the milk yield satisfactory? What change is occurring in the condition of the cows? These are questions a stockman will continually be asking. Loss of flesh, for example, can be an indication of underfeeding, not perhaps in total food, but in actual nutrients consumed. For a short period, loss of flesh may be sound husbandry, but this condition should not be allowed to proceed so far as to impair the health or stamina of the cow, her breeding regularity or the quality of her milk.

Now we come to a more detailed consideration of the use of the feeding standards that have been discussed.

Dealing with maintenance requirements first, these are generally met by foods which we classify as roughages (such as hay or straw) or succulents (such as roots). The composition of these foods is given in the Appendix IV, but such foods can be simply compared on a hay basis as shown in Table 8.6.

Table 8.6.

1 kg medium-quality hay equals:
  3 kg medium-quality silage (grass)
  3 kg arable silage
  4 kg kale or beet tops
  5 kg mangolds or swedes
  3 kg fodder-beet or potatoes
  3–5 kg dried beet pulp
  0·75 kg dried grass (crude protein 14 per cent or less)
  0·5 kg straw plus 0·25 kg straw balancer
  1 kg wet grains plus 0·25 kg cereals.

Substitutes for Hay

The maintenance requirements of the various breeds in terms of medium quality hay have already been given in Table 8.1; that table, used in conjunction with Table 8.6, makes it possible to work out a maintenance ration according to the farm foods available. For example, Table 8.1 shows that a Friesian cow needs a maintenance ration of approximately 9·5 kg of hay. She could be fed with part-hay ration of hay and the balance made up by any single one of the substitute foods mentioned–in appropriate quantity—or a combination of any of these foods, again in appropriate quantities. On an all-silage farm the hay could be completely replaced by silage.

For example: *9·5 kg hay equals:*

  4·5 kg hay   6·5 kg hay
     plus   *or*   plus   *or* 28·5 kg silage.
  15 kg silage   12 kg kale

A wide range of maintenance rations could be worked out in this way.

  With the advent of silage, many herds have been fed on an all-silage ration for both maintenance and production. However, with high-yielding herds—i.e. above six thousand litres—there is a case for inclusion of some hay in the ration, its role being that of rumen conditioner.

Milk from Maintenance Foods

The production requirement of low-yielding cows may be met by feeding more of the foods commonly fed for maintenance, provided the energy and protein content are sufficiently high.

Table 8.7. Production Value of Roughage and Succulent Foods

To produce 1 litre of average (3·7 per cent BF) milk feed:

0·7 kg medium-quality hay
2·1 kg medium-quality silage
2·8 kg kale or beet tops
3·5 kg mangolds
0·5 kg dried grass, medium quality
1·6 kg brewers' grains.

The value of maintenance foods to the high-yielding cow is limited by the ability of the cow to take in dry matter. The maintenance type foods simply are not rich enough in either energy or protein to supply a high level of milk yield.

The best use of maintenance-type foods for milk production is in mid to late lactation. It is possible to take maintenance and up to 12·5 litres from silage with cows in late lactation. In early lactation it must be recognised that maintenance-type foods can only do that particular task.

As dairy costs continue to rise, both fixed and variable, so level of yield must increase and be produced as economically as possible.

Once the approximate balance of a maintenance ration has been carried out, the finer balancing of the ration can be carried out, using a full-scale ME, DCP and dry-matter evaluation.

In general, with a hay ration, the likely limiting factor is the availability of energy and protein, whereas with a full silage ration, protein is likely to be available, with lack of energy providing a constraint.

Fibre and Bulk Control

Aiming at higher yields, the dairy farmer may wish to move from 4500 to 5500 litres and higher; there is a danger of including too little fibre in the ration. A minimal level of 2–3 kg of hay is necessary for the high-yielding cow. First-cut silages and spring grass both have low fibres, and their use, coupled with high levels of concentrates—up to 12–14 kg per day—can lead to a low level of butterfat.

With reference to supply of bulk food, mention has been made that a ration containing too many bulky foods contains too little energy and protein. The alternative could be a high level of concentrate foods supplemented by too little bulk. Cows are usually eager to eat concentrate foods in preference to fibrous bulk foods. Provided the production foods are taken up, there should be an ample supply of bulk foods available for the cow to take as necessary. The best example of this is in self-feed silage where cows are always able to satisfy their body requirements and always maintain body condition.

A Food Classification

In order to concentrate the diet of high-yielding cows and render that diet readily digestible, we need to use feedingstuffs high in digestible nutrients and low in fibre. Such foods are commonly known as concentrates and include cereal grains, oil cakes and so on. The available foods can be classified as in Table 8.8.

It should be noted that high-quality dried grass is classified as a concentrate only when its fibre content is below 20 per cent, irrespective of its crude protein content.

In the fifties and sixties there was a great deal of interest in the home-mixing of bought-in concentrate foods for the production ration. A combination of several factors has had the effect of reducing much of the home-mixing:

1. With herds increasing in size, the labour on many farms has been matched to the efficient running of these larger units, and labour has not been spare to carry out the mixing.

2. In recent years the amount of capital investment necessary in new milling and mixing plant has been such as to reduce the interest in the project.

On grassland farms in the West, where there has been a move to silage, this has been widely supplemented by bought-in balanced concentrates for the greater part of production.

With silage having a good level of protein, it has been usual to feed cereals in the form of rolled mineralised barley for the first 5–10 litres of milk on top of the silage on a feed fence.

COMPLETE FEEDING

The mixing of concentrates on the farm has been given new impetus in recent years by the introduction of complete feeding. The system is based on the theory that if she is on a total diet of roughage and concentrate foods together, the cow will eat as much of the complete mix as she needs for production. It is a system widely practised in the USA and Israel. The home-grown constituents in the ration

Table 8.8. Classification of feedingstuffs in ascending order of 'concentration'

Group A *Roughages (low concentration)* *Fibre percentage 25 per cent or over* Cereal straws (oats and barley only) Hay (average or below) Low-quality silage Low-quality dried grass or lucerne	*Remarks* Derived from mature plant tissues, suitable only for 'maintenance' purposes
Group B *Succulents and high-quality roughage* *(medium concentration)* *Fibre percentage 15–24 per cent* First-quality hay (e.g. tripod hay) Grass and arable silage Root crops Kale and sugar-beet tops	*Remarks* Suitable for maintenance and for low-level production
Group C *Concentrates (highly concentrated)* *Fibre percentage below 15 per cent* Cereal grains and dredge corn Milling offals Distillers' and brewers' grains High-quality dried grass (below 20 per cent fibre) Oil cakes and meals Meat and fish meals	*Remarks* Essential foods for high production

can be hay, straw, silage supplemented by barley, oats and wheat. Bought-in foods include brewers' grains, molassed pressed pulp, and concentrate foods such as maize, soya bean and fishmeal.

Complete feeding is based upon the ME system and has developed into a very complex subject. It is perhaps most suited to the arable farms of the east where there are many arable by-products available. The system has brought the idea of home mixing back to the forefront of dairy cow feeding, and is known to work well in the type of situation mentioned.

Complete feeding is very dependent on reliable but expensive feeder wagons. In this system cows tend to be fed better than on traditional systems and yields do increase. Unfortunately, in most situations, no attention is given to monitoring inputs closely and margins have proved to be very disappointing. The system gives a better fermentation pattern in the rumen and butterfats tend to improve.

Readers who wish to have more detailed information should consult *Complete Diets for Cattle and Sheep* by Professor John Owen, published by Farming Press.

IMPORTANCE OF MINERALS

The mineral content of the diet is important. With farm-mixed foods a mineral mixture needs to be incorporated. There are many commercial mixtures available to meet any situation. Most oil cakes are rich in phosphorous relative to calcium, whereas most grassland products, hay, silage, dried grass and beet pulp are rich in calcium and low in phosphorus. Compound cakes are fortified by the necessary minerals.

Gross mineral deficiencies are unlikely to be found on farms where good husbandry is practised, even when production is obtained largely from home grown non-concentrate foods. In some areas trace-element deficiencies (e.g. copper) are known to exist.

The indiscriminate addition of minerals to a cow's diet is to be deprecated. When in doubt, veterinary services should always be contacted.

The chief mineral deficiencies occurring today in order of frequency are as shown in Table 8.9.

Table 8.9. Mineral Deficiencies

Condition	Deficiency	Prevention
Lactation tetany	magnesium	Add 57 g per day calcined magnesite to concentrate ration
Pining Failure to thrive Dull coat	cobalt or copper	Feed suitable reinforced mineral mixture under veterinary advice
Goitre Swollen glands Infertility	iodine	

Vitamins

On the farm, the most likely symptoms of mineral deficiencies are indicated by a depraved appetite and skeletal weakness in milking cows. If the assimilation of lime and phosphorus into the blood stream and thence to the skeleton is to be efficient, the provision of adequate minerals in the diet of milking cows or young calves must be associated with adequate supplies of Vitamin D. The cow and the calf can both manufacture their own Vitamin D under the effect of direct sunlight, but in winter when they are housed, Vitamin D deficiency can be avoided by feeding them good sun-cured hay or cod-liver oil or synthetic preparations of Vitamins A and D in powder form, as a safeguard against rickets. Usual rate of addition is 2·2 kg synthetic vitamins mix per tonne of concentrates.

The direct addition of vitamins to the cows' diet—except in respect of Vitamins A and D (see above)—is not usual or necessary provided the diet is composed of a basis of good-quality home-grown foods, particularly hay, silage, and dried grass. Green foods providing the yellow colour in the milk have a high B carotene content—the precursor of Vitamin A and has an important function of its own in relation to fertility.

Compound Concentrates

The majority of milk production is obtained by feeding one or other of a wide range of commercially compounded foods. They are available in several categories.

High-energy Compounds
This type of compound has an ME of approximately 13·4 MJ and is fed to high-yielding cows at a level of 0·35 kg/litre. It is often associated with a high level of protein of the order of 18 per cent. Research in recent years suggests that one of the limiting factors in high-level milk production is the low level of protein. Certain high-energy compounds have a low protein and are particularly designed to be used for cows at grass.

High Energy compounds usually contain a higher percentage of oil with 6·7% being the maximum to maintain good physical quality. Too much oil interferes with fibre digestion in the rumen. Oil in the diet provides about half the butterfat provided in the udder, but it should be of the correct type.

Medium-Energy Compounds

This type of feed will have a MJ/kg of approximately 12·5 and would be fed at a rate of 0·4 kg/litre. This type of compound can be satisfactorily used in herds with averages up to the 5400 litre level. Above this level, higher energy foods are required.

Modern concentrates are made up on a least-cost formulation system so the actual constituents do vary from time to time.

The choice between buying in concentrates or home mixing is very much related to the type, size of farm and all the resources available, particularly labour and capital.

RESEARCH INTO RUMINANT DIGESTION

Recent work has focused attention on the importance of the 'physical texture' of food consumed by the cow in its effect on the production of fatty acids by bacterial fermentation in the rumen or first stomach.

Roughage foods tend to promote acetic acid production, whereas concentrates tend to promote propionic or butyric acid production. Acetic acid encourages butterfat, whereas propionic or butyric acid encourage higher solids-not-fat production, so that the balance of roughage to concentrates in the diet of the cow can influence milk composition. Roughage foods which are finely ground (i.e. the fibre is then no longer in the long state) act similarly to concentrates. So, for example, to maintain butterfat percentage the milling of dried grass would be inadvisable.

CHAPTER 9

PLANNING TO FEED THE DAIRY HERD IN WINTER

IN the last chapter the scientific basis of feeding dairy cows was discussed. These basic standards can be put to use in the planning of feed for a dairy herd over a winter period.

The maintenance needs of the different liveweight categories were given in Table 8.1 in terms of medium-quality hay. If such quantities are related to the total requirements over a 180-day winter, the following table shows the approximate amounts of hay needed to supply the requirements of a standard ration for M + 5 litres and M + 10 litres.

Table 9.1. Approximate Winter Feed Requirements (in kilograms of hay)

Liveweight kg	Breed type	For maintenance kg	Maintenance + 5 litres milk	Maintenance + 10 litres milk
660	South Devon	1880	2540	3200
559	Dairy Shorthorn British Friesian	1676	2235	2794
508	Devon Red Poll Welsh Black	1524	2083	2642
457	Ayrshire Guernsey	1372	2032 2083	2693 2794
381	Jersey Kerry	1219	1930	2642

The varying acreage required to provide the quantities of food at differing yields per hectare can readily be calculated. For example, at 3766 kg hay per hectare, for maintenance needs only this varies from 0·32 hectares with Jerseys (3·1 cows/hectare) to 0·45 hectares with Friesians (2·2 cows/hectare). Hay can be expressed in terms of other food, as shown in the 'hay equivalent' system given earlier in Chapter 8.

If a cow required 10 kg hay for maintenance per head per day for a 180-day winter, this would mean 1800 kg total requirement, i.e. 1·8 tonnes hay. Where hay was completely replaced by silage the requirement would be $1·8 \times 3 = 5·4$ tonnes silage for the 180-day winter.

FEED AVAILABLE PER COW

When planning the winter-feed requirements, it is necessary to assess as accurately as possible the total quantity of feed on the farm available for the dairy herd as a whole. Ideally, this assessment of available foods should be carried out by mid-summer. If there is any likely shortfall, then there is still adequate time to sow catch crops or buy in bulk food, such as hay or brewers' grains.

Young stock can, if in regular ages, be reckoned as requiring per head, one-half of the food required per cow, so that forty cows and twenty followers are equivalent to fifty cows.

Silage, hay, and roots can be estimated by measurement of the clamps or stacks, using the density per cubic metre given in Appendix II.

Example Farms

Let us now consider the winter-feed position on some example farms.

Table 9.2. Farm A. Mainly grass—stocking 40 cows and 30 followers (55 cow equivalents); breed: British Friesians.

Feeds available	As hay equivalent (tonnes)	Area per cow (hectares)
Silage—16 hectares (203 tonnes)	67·1	2·2 cows per
Hay—4 hectares (15 tonnes)	15·2	hectare (0·45
Kale—4 hectares (163 tonnes)	40·6	hectare) per
	——	cow
	123·0	equivalent
	or 122,940 kg	

Hay per cow equivalent 122,940 kg ÷ 55 cow equ. = 2235 kg per cow.

On this farm, therefore, the winter feeding plan can allow for feeding the herd to a level of M + 5 litres from these home-grown 'bulk' feeds.

Table 9.3. Farm B. Mixed arable—stocking 50 cows (flying herd)—breed: Ayrshire.

Feeds available	As hay equivalent (tonnes)	Area per cow
Silage—12 hectares (152·4 tonnes)	50·8	
Hay—6 hectares (25·4 tonnes)	25·4	0·36 hectare
Beet tops ⎱ as required Barley straw ⎰		

The total feed requirements at the M + 5 litres level for fifty Ayrshire cows is 101·6 tonnes (see Table 9.1) as hay equivalent. Of this, 76·2 tonnes are provided by hay and silage, leaving a requirement of 25·4 tonnes as barley straw and beet tops. Suitable rations would thus be provided by 81·3 tonnes beet tops (= 20·3 tonnes hay equivalent) and 10·2 tonnes barley straw (5·1 tonnes hay equivalent).

It will be noted that by using arable crop by-products in this way the actual acreage of land solely devoted to the production of cow feed has been cut to 0·36 hectare per cow.

This check on the feed position before the winter begins is a very necessary part of managing a dairy herd. The basic requirement is to prepare a winter feed plan in the spring, assessing possible silage cuts, hay crops, root crops, etc. If the climate is unsuitable and it is obvious that the requirements are not going to be met, then it is advisable to alter Plan A to Plan B and make further alterations as seem necessary. The last thing that any farmer should do is to run out of winter fodder. Buying bulk food during late winter is very expensive. During recent hard winters the value of hay rose from £40 per tonne in October to £90 per tonne in February.

PLANNING DAY TO DAY FEEDING

Once the total food supply is secured and known, then the day-to-day feeding programme can be finalised. Certain foods such as hay and silage can be fed all winter as required. Others, such as kale and beet tops have a much shorter period of use—damage by frost means using such crops before the hard weather starts.

The milking herd on a North
Devon farm (Exmoor in the
distance) grazing the last
week in November.

November grass. Late grass
production on a Sussex farm.

Direct drilling of kale. In this instance the seed was sown mid-June by a Rotaseeder; photographed at the end of the month, the plants appear well advanced.

Cattle grazing Maris Kestrel kale, which was direct drilled on June 26th into an S.22 Italian ryegrass ley after a silage cut.

ICI photo

On farm A the plan was to feed hay with kale, eventually substituting with self-feed silage.

Total hay equivalent of all feed is 123 tonnes, which over 180 days allows 0·68 tonnes/day.

So hay and kale providing 55·9 tonnes will last for 80–85 days and silage at 67·1 tonnes for 95–100 days. The daily quantities are as shown in Table 9.4.

Table 9.4.

Early winter		Late winter	
1 Oct.–25 Dec.		25 Dec.–31 March	
Kale	36–9 kg	Silage	36–9 kg
Hay	3–4 kg		

On farm B the plan might be to feed hay and barley straw in equal proportions to the beet tops and then hay with the silage.

On this plan, 10·2 tonnes barley straw, 10·2 tonnes hay and 81 tonnes of beet tops will provide 35·6 tonnes of hay equivalent, sufficient for sixty-four days, or two months, and hay with silage will be fed for the remaining four months. The daily quantities would then be as shown in Table 9.5.

Table 9.5.

Early winter		Late winter	
1 Oct.–30 Nov.		1 Dec.–31 March	
Beet tops	25 kg	Silage	25 kg
Hay	3 kg	Hay	2–3 kg
Barley straw	3 kg		

The changeover in both herds from kale and beet tops to silage feeding should be made gradually over the space of five to seven days.

The winter feeding has been reckoned to 31 March. Early bite on some farms is available before this. It is advisable to plan for a longer winter and certainly in the North it would be better to budget for a 210-day period.

Quality in Home-Grown Feeds

The above examples illustrate how winter feeding can be planned on individual farms in order to avoid waste of feed resources, or on the other hand, to avoid underfeeding of the cows, provided at least that the quality of the home-grown feed (silage, hay and straw, if used) is at least up to the feeding values given in Appendix IV.

How can one check on this? By chemical analyses carried out by ADAS and commercial firms, a guide can be obtained on feeding values, otherwise it is a matter of learning from the cows themselves.

If quality of feed is low, milk yields will fail to be maintained, and the cows will lose body weight. Under prolonged underfeeding, the SNF percentage in the milk falls significantly.

In severe weather, kale and beet tops lose palatability if frosted or contaminated with soil, but otherwise show less variation in feeding value than hay or silage.

If hay fed in either of the examples was very poor, the deficiency in energy could be remedied by feeding 1 kg of rolled barley, oats or sugar beet nuts.

The Problem of Milk from Bulk Feeds

Because of the difficulty of ensuring uniformly high quality in home-grown bulk feeds owing to the hazards of weather (even silage-making requires reasonably dry weather), farmers have found it easier to practise to achieve M + 5 litres level of feeding than a greater level of milk from bulk feeds. High production of milk from bulk feeds involves a reduced stocking rate, as the area needed for the production of the extra food rises, assuming a constant level of crop yield.

Table 9.1. shows that the requirement for a change from maintenance only to maintenance plus 10 litres would need an increase in the area required of up to 70 per cent.

At the same time, high levels of bulk feeding limits yield because of the digestive capacity of the cow. Low-quality bulk feeds tend to depress appetite because of their relatively high fibre content.

With high-yielding dairy cows, both in terms of milk yield and compositional quality of the milk, it is necessary to limit the amount of bulk feeds; the ration has to be 'energy rich'. This means replacing some of the bulk foods and substituting concentrate feeds. In practical terms more energy can be put into a ration when the concentrate fed is changed from a rate of 0·4 kg/litre to 0·35 kg/litre.

Protein-Sparing Function of Bulk Feeds

If bulk feeds are of high quality, the protein content of the concentrates fed for production over the level for which the bulk feeds are considered adequate can be reduced. This will be discussed with reference to self-feed silage in Chapter 10, and would apply to Farm A in the previous example.

To sum up, on the majority of dairy farms today it is reasonable to plan for winter bulk feeding to a level of maintenance plus five litres of milk.

Economy of production associated with the cheaper bulk feeds is then attained without loss of yield per cow by overloading her digestive capacity. This could well occur if excessive levels of bulk feed were fed, except in the case of low-yielding cows.

In general, controlled feeding on an individual or even a group basis pays good rewards with cows capable of lactation over five thousand litres. On the other hand, with cows that are genetically incapable of achieving higher yields, then by all means feed as cheaply as possible, both in the type of foods fed and in the system of feeding.

Table 9.6. Examples of Typical Winter Rations

	350–400 kg			Liveweight 400–450 kg			500–550 kg		
	M	M + 5	M + 10	M	M + 5	M + 10	M	M + 5	M + 10
1. Hay kg	6·3	9·9	—	7·2	10·8	—	9·07	12·2	—
2. Hay	3·2	3·2	3·2	3·2	3·2	3·2	3·2	3·2	3·2
Kale or Beet tops	12·7	25	25	15·8	31·7	31·7	25	38	38
Cereals	—	—	1·8	—	—	1·8	—	—	1·8
3. Hay	3·2	3·2	3·2	3·2	3·2	3·2	3·2	3·2	3·2
Silage	9·5	20	20	12·7	25	25	18	27·2	27·2
Cereals	—	—	1·8	—	—	1·8	—	—	1·8
4. Silage	19·0	29·9	29·9	21·7	32·6	32·6	27·2	38·1	38·1
Cereals	—	—	1·8	—	—	1·8	—	—	1·8

As an example of feeding for high yields the Table 9.7 illustrates the management applied by the author to a Friesian cow which gave 454 litres of milk in one week—an average of 64·8 litres per day. The livewight of the cow was 660 kg and the dry matter intake was 3·48 per cent of the liveweight.

When any cow gives this level of milk it is important to appreciate that the cow is an outstanding converter of food into milk and goes

Table 9.7. Feeding Schedule

5.30 am—4·5 kg concentrates (high energy)
milking
1·8 kg hay (very good quality)

10.00 am—2·7 kg concentrates (high energy)
1·4 kg sugar-beet pulp—moist

2.00 pm—4·5 kg concentrates (high energy)
milking
1·8 kg hay (very good quality)

4.00 pm—2·7 kg concentrates
1·4 kg sugar-beet pulp—moist

9.00 pm—4·5 kg concentrates (high energy)
milking
1·8 kg hay (very good quality)

beyond this to the extent of losing considerable weight during early lactation, well in excess of 0·5 kg per day.

There must be considerable effort made to restore this body weight during mid to late lactation. This can best be achieved by providing only the highest quality of bulk feeds, silage and hay. Cows on self-feed silage can make up their appetite and regain weight. It is vital in modern feed systems where bulk feed is carried to the cow, that the cow is never left short of feed.

The rations in this chapter have been formulated using a simple hay equivalent basis. With the advent of the new ME system, it could be suggested that the hay equivalent system is outdated. It does, however, still help in a practical way to arrive quickly at the possible combinations of home-grown foods which can be blended to give a maintenance or maintenance plus 5 litre type ration. Once the rough approximation has been arrived at, the finer detail of the ration can be assessed on the ME system. However, care must be taken.

The value of bulk feeds is so variable that it is quite likely that when a ration is fed, the result is different from that required. In this case, every dairyman should realise that it is highly likely that his ration is wrong and that the cow is more likely to give a correct assessment of the ration.

The feeding of cows is always likely to contain something of an art and is unlikely ever to be one hundred per cent science-based.

CHAPTER 10

HERD MANAGEMENT IN WINTER

WE have seen how to plan for the winter feeding of the dairy herd and the scientific principles involved. The next step is to consider the day-to-day management of the dairy herd.

From the examples of rations given in the last chapter it would logically follow that a herd has to be split into several groups in order to get the best out of the available foods. The requirements of a cow differ considerably at different stages of lactation.

The cow in early lactation requires a high-energy diet, little milk being taken from bulk feed. Mid-lactation cows can take some milk from bulk feeds, late-lactation cows can take up to 12·5 litres from silage at the end of the winter.

A Grouping Plan

For planning the day-to-day feeding routine, a first step would be to divide the herd into three groups.

A—Dry cows and in-calf heifers within two months of calving.

B—Freshly calved cows and heifers in the first four months of lactation during which half of the total lactation yield will be given.

C—Cows and heifers safely in calf and in late lactation.

As far as possible these groups should be yarded separately. The principles to be borne in mind when feeding these different groups are summarised as follows:

A—A good basal ration should be fed, equivalent to a ration for at least maintenance plus five litres. In some cases concentrates could be fed where cows were not in good body condition before calving.

149

B—Fed for high production. Bulky foods must be of high quality and controlled in quantity.

C—Fed largely on bulk foods to appetite level.

This means in effect that the control of food consumed must be carefully carried out with Group B, where each cow needs to be treated not as a member of a group as in A and C, but fed individually.

Individual feeding is desirable for proper management of cows in early lactation, except where the level of milk yield is very low. With the general use of the AI service on farms for over twenty-five years it could be assumed that the genetic potential of the national dairy herd has increased considerably during this time.

Managing a Herd with a Good Genetic Yield Potential
A possible constraint on the ability of a cow to give higher yields of milk is likely to be feeding and management. Better feeding in early lactation will produce high yields. The other important factor to consider is that high yields should be obtained with the most economic usage of bought-in energy foods.

Cutting Feed Costs
By dividing the herd as suggested, the dairyman is given the opportunity to make the best use of home-produced bulk feeds. The general approach to feeding cows should be that those giving high yields are fed well and lower-yielding cows are made to produce on bulk feeds.

The essential management feature needed to arrive at and maintain a successful feeding policy is to record production on a regular weekly basis and attempt to correlate the milk yield with the food fed.

In early lactation, high yields are inevitably associated with a high level of feeding. The objectives of the first one hundred days of lactation are that the cow should attain a good peak yield of between twenty-five and thirty litres. Body weight loss must be minimised to enable the cow to conceive to first service. Once the cow is in-calf, the milk yield tends to drop. The requirement then is to reduce the proportion of expensive bought-in food and increase that of relatively cheaper home-grown food, at the same time making sure that the milk yield does not fall at a rate faster than is normally acceptable. Dr Broster of NIRD has suggested that a fall of $2\frac{1}{2}$ per cent is the normal expectation. With good-quality bulk feed the replacement rate of bulk for concentrates can be increased. If quality of bulk is poor then little replacement can be carried out.

The essential exercise is the matching of milk yield and feed input. This can only be achieved by regular monitoring of milk yield. In addition to showing clearly the value and effect of a feed programme, regular weekly milk recording also highlights problems which occur in the different groups of cows which calve each month. Once problems have been identified, they can be solved.

FOLDING GREEN CROPS

Earlier reference was made to forage farming in Chapter 6. This will help to reduce feed costs.

The chief crops used are the brassicas such as marrow-stem and thousand-head kale and rape. They can either be sown broadcast or in drills. My practice with early April/May-sown kale is to drill in 46 cm rows with the fourth spout of a four-row drill sowing hungry-gap kale, so that six rows of either marrow-stem or thousand-headed kale alternate with two rows of hungry-gap kale. The latter, being of shorter growth, provides a ready-made avenue up which the wire of the electric fence can be run.

Drilling is generally parallel to the shortest side of field. Later in the season, where the soil has been thoroughly cultivated and cleaned, kale and rape can be sown broadcast either by hand or with a corn drill with the spouts lifted. After early potatoes, kale or rape can follow as a catch crop.

In a wet winter, muddy gateways can be a problem to folding off kale. Alternative means of access to the kale, other than through only one gateway are an advantage and, where possible, a lie-back in a field of turf or stubble is well worth consideration.

For instance, after taking an early hay or silage crop in the last year of a ley, a portion of the field could be ploughed immediately, sown to kale, and the whole field eventually ploughed for spring corn after the cows have grazed the kale and used the unploughed portion for lying down.

In frosty weather the grazing of kale or rape is attended with some risk. This can be reduced by first giving a feed of hay or dry fodder. In really hard weather resort should be made to silage as the source of succulent feed rather than risk the chances of digestive upsets through folding green crops.

A further alternative is to harvest the kale with a forage harvester and feed lacerated kale in mangers. An offset forage harvester is advisable to avoid soil contamination.

Observations and recordings made by the author and by NAAS officers on the consumption of kale crops indicate that the following guides can be offered in determining the acreage to be grown per cow and the daily consumption.

Kale consumed per hour is usually about 11·3–13·6 kg, sufficient generally as a production ration for 5 litres of milk. But this consumption figure is only found where the cows are freshly turned into a new fold. On a kale stubble previously folded, consumption per hour would fall below this level.

Under free-range folding (i.e. where consumption is unrestricted) the average 508–599 kg cow consumes up to 38 kg of kale in three hours' grazing. This seems to be the limit of her capacity and appetite.

An alternative method of rationing kale consumed is by time. Fence off about 0·8 hectare and restrict the grazing to two periods of, say, one to two hours each.

Rationing by area is a convenient method and a field which is both long and narrow is most suitable. Depth will vary according to the weight of the crop and the amount one wants to feed, but a depth of two or three rows helps to avoid fouling.

Depth of fold according to crop yield—allowing two metres of line per cow—is given in Table 10.1

Table 10.1. Depth of Fold

Yields per hectare (tonne)	Depth of fold in metres when consuming per day:		
	12·7 kg	25·4 kg	38·1 kg
20·08 (rape)	3·16 (63)	6·32 (126)	9·48 (189)
40·17 (kale)	1·58 (32)	3·16 (63)	4·74 (95)
60·26 (kale)	1·05 (21)	2·11 (42)	3·16 (63)

(Square metres per ten cows given in brackets)

Whatever method of grazing is adopted, there is a tendency for the cows to clear off the leafy parts of the kale on the first day and to be left with the stumps only on the next. Milk yields can vary unless the fold is moved daily.

Assuming, therefore, a 15·2 tonne crop and a winter consumption of 25 kg kale daily per cow for 120 days, each cow will require 3 tonne—0·4 hectare per five cows.

Where kale folding is practicable, I would make this further suggestion: that the total acreage be divided equally between marrow-stem and thousand-head kale, eaten off in that order. This method makes the best use of the greater frost-resistance of the latter and its greater retention of leaf as the winter progresses.

Rape, in view of its low frost resistance, should always be eaten off before kale. Italian or HI ryegrass sown with trefoil is another catch crop suitable for folding, particularly under spring corn. A top dressing with nitrogen after harvest can be relied upon to give a copious growth in November and December.

USE CONVENIENT FIELDS

However, a word of warning is necessary whenever winter grazing is planned. Aim to reduce to a minimum the distance the cows have to walk. A heavy milking cow is already working hard, and if in addition she is made into a beast of burden, milk yields will undoubtedly suffer.

I believe that winter-grazing crops might well be fitted into a short rotation on fields conveniently accessible to the cows. I have used winter-grazing crops of kale two years in succession, followed by a two-year ley of HI ryegrass and late-flowering red clover. This is designed to give both early and late grazing. The fields used are convenient to the cows, well-fenced and watered.

As broad guide on which the details of successful cow management can be based, I summarise below the recommendations so far given:

1. It is desirable to house high-yielding cows to reduce their maintenance requirements, to reduce feeding costs, and to enable controlled feeding to be carried out.

2. Out-wintering is rarely advised even with low-yielding cows and cows in late lactation, and even then is suitable only when sheltered land is available. A policy of summer milk production should be considered where no adequate housing is available.

3. Provided certain safeguards are taken, the grazing of arable crops reduces feed costs in comparison with the labour of cutting and carting fodder.

4. Decide on a convenient daily routine and keep to it consistently. Cows hate to be kept waiting for their food or to be unduly disturbed from their normal habits.

5. Where cows are to be fed as a group rather than as individuals (e.g. at pasture or grazing kale), allow plenty of feeding room per cow and make appropriate allowance for wasted food which is trampled underfoot. Close rationing of cows under these conditions is impossible.

6. Do not make your cows beasts of burden, else a great deal of energy expended in walking long distances will mean less milk. Watch the comfort of the cows.

SELF-FEEDING OF SILAGE
(totally inwintered herds)

Self-feeding of silage offers considerable opportunities to cut labour cost, provided the layout is well planned and slurry disposal adequate. The system requires concentrating on silage-making to the extent of providing 1 tonne of silage per cow per month (1·53 m^3 of silo capacity).

Depth of silage should not exceed 1·83 m and with 24-hour access, there should be 18–23 cm per cow of silage face, depending upon the breed of cow. If other bulk feeds are available then this may be slightly reduced. If cows are fed in batches, then 0·6–0·8 m of feed face should be allowed.

The simplest control for the cow at the face is an electrified wire.

The system does not allow individual feeding. It is also possible for timid cows and possibly heifers to be subjected to bullying.

Self-feeding is a solution to the problem of reducing labour cost, without at the same time reducing yield per cow. The basis of the system is a good-quality silage of about 23–25 per cent dry matter, with good digestibility and a uniform fermentation.

The facilities for storing silage vary greatly from farm to farm. Some farms use one large silage clamp for all the silage cuts, up to three. In other situations, separate buildings are used for the different cuts. Where just the single barn is available, a Dorset Wedge method may be used. In this way it is often the latest cut silage that is eaten first and the better first cut eaten in the later part of the winter. This does fit in with providing quality silage which will produce milk when fed to late-lactation cows at the end of the winter.

The self-feed system is a group system of feeding, so individual supplementary feeding has to be carried out in the milking parlour. The amount of supplementary feeding varies according to the silage quality, the level of milk yield per cow and the stage of lactation.

Where the level of feeding has been improved, yields have risen and it has been necessary in many cases to introduce a simple feed fence. This is a development which can be simply explained in the case of a cow giving 30 litres of milk and taking no milk from silage in early lactation (i.e. M + 0).

The concentrates required at the rate of 0·4 kg/litre would be

12 kg. Up to 5 kg concentrates would be fed at each parlour milking, leaving 2 kg of concentrates to be fed down the feed fence in the middle of the day. This development also fits in with current research findings that concentrates should be fed 'little and often': perhaps two or even three times per day on the feed fence in addition to parlour feeding. The spread of feeding allows a better fermentation process to take place in the rumen; the pH is at a steady level instead of having violent fluctuations which tend to depress butterfat.

The concentrates on the feed fence can be of a cereal nature—barley, which is cheaper than compound cakes and also helps to utilise the high protein level available in good silage, over and above that required for a maintenance requirement. Sugar beet nuts are a very good source of concentrate to be used on the feed fence for the first 5–10 litres.

With high-yielding herds it may be necessary to feed for up to twenty litres on the feed fence; the last ten litres would need to be provided for in the form of high-energy compound concentrates.

The quality of silage, supplementary feeding in the parlour and on a feed fence are all factors involved in obtaining the optimal yield from any herd at the most favourable economic level. There is no definite answer, it is something to be sought for each year given our variable climate and its effect on quality and quantity of silage available.

Rate of Supplementary Feeding

As a general guide, rates of feeding depend upon silage quality (to be checked by silage analysis) and quantity eaten, and the yield of milk, as shown in Table 10.2.

Table 10.2. Rates of Feeding

Milk from Bulk feed	Milk yield per cow per day (litres)				
	10	15	20	25	30
	Concentrates to be fed per day (kg)				
M + 0	4	6	8	10	12
M + 2·5	3	5	7	9	11
M + 5	2	4	6	8	10
M + 7·5	1	3	5	7	9
M + 10·0	—	2	4	6	8
M + 12·5	—	1	3	5	7
M + 15·0	—	—	2	4	6

As can be seen from the table, given a silage of an established quality by analysis, the level of supplementary is varied according to the amount of milk given. When the appropriate level of concentrates has been fed, the cows on self-feed silage have the facility to satisfy their appetites on the silage face. With the same quality silage through the winter, as the milk yield decreases so the supplementary feeds can be curtailed. If the silage face improves in quality, as in the Dorset Wedge system where the cows move from third to second to first cut, this improvement should be turned into more milk from silage and again a reduction in supplementary feeding.

The table can be used where cows are at grass. For example, where a December-calved cow was giving 20 litres of milk and taking 15 litres from grass, she would require a supplementary feed of 2 kg of concentrate food; this could be wholely cereal or sugar beet pulp nuts.

With this type of herd, the aim would be to use silage, late cut, at a stage to give maximum bulk which would provide a cheap winter feed.

Easy-Feed System

The easy-feed system of silage feeding is the logical development which farmers have to consider when the cow numbers in a herd grow beyond the level where the cows have the necessary width on the self-feed silage face. The system involves the provision of a feed fence, providing 0·8 m per cow. The silage is put out once per day with the use of a self-unloading trailer. The merit of the system is the ease with which any supplementary feed can be given. It is possible to provide self-locking yokes along the length of the feed fence where individual feeding is required outside the parlour.

It is desirable that the fence should be covered and illuminated otherwise the usefulness of the system cannot be fully exploited. There is the obvious requirement for additional building capital but this has to be weighed against the possibility of more cows being kept and the greater degree of control over the feeding of the groups of cows. The feed fence also gives greater flexibility in terms of feeding foods other than silage, such as hay, kale and potatoes, and is particularly useful in the spring and autumn periods when fields are likely to be poached by grazing and grass can be brought into the system—a simple seasonal form of zero grazing.

The general system of zero grazing is a method whereby grass is cut all through the grazing season and brought to the cows by a form of self-unloading forage box. The system is expensive in equipment but saves fencing and laying on water to fields. Fields inaccessible, or too distant for grazing, can be put down to grass and intensively utilised. Production per hectare is claimed to be 7 to 10 per cent higher than in normal grazing systems; there is less waste of grass due to soiling. Criticism of the method arises from the high machinery costs involved and the large requirement for labour.

Complete Feeding

The system of complete feeding has been used in the United States and Israel for many years. In the United Kingdom, the system was introduced in the late seventies. The system for many farmers was simply an extension of the idea of feeding a high-energy food little and often as in the case with herds on easy feed silage.

The concept of a total diet is to give the cows a complete mix of available foods—silage, cereals, brewers' grains, straw and concentrates—which will provide for the total requirements of the cow in her expected dry matter intake. The total energy within the mix 'M' (i.e. total MJ) compared to the kg of DM matter intake D gives the M/D or the energy concentration of the mixture. This is required to be between 8 and 12 MJ according to the stage of lactation.

The density also has to be related to the level of milk yield. The mix should have a DCP of 11–12 per cent and a minimum fibre level of 14 per cent.

The system can eliminate parlour feeding and therefore allows milking to be carried out without reference to feeding policy.

The mixer wagons used in the systems can be fitted with load cells which allows accurate weighing of all feed on a group basis, but not to individual cows; the groups of cows are fed once per day. On the large arable farm which has many by-products, the system offers scope for feed economies. However, these tend to be balanced by the increasing level of machinery running costs and depreciation.

The system seems to offer considerable scope in increasing cow yields and compositional quality of milk, but to be financially successful the energy, dry-matter intake, protein and fibre levels need to be very carefully monitored.

CHAPTER 11

HERD MANAGEMENT IN THE SUMMER

WELL-MANAGED grassland is the cheapest source of cattle food any dairy farmer can have. At the same time, good grassland farming is one of the best ways of maintaining and enhancing soil fertility.

Therefore, on every dairy farm, grass should be regarded as the most important crop. Properly managed, it can give a far greater cash return per hectare than many cash crops.

Before outlining the details of successful grass management, three broad problems need stating.

EXTEND THE GRAZING SEASON

First, grass is seasonal in growth with a spring flush in May and a less marked flush in autumn; weather conditions influence the extent of the flush and the period over which it is maintained.

Secondly, there are marked changes in the feeding value of grass during its growing season. It can vary from being equivalent to a form of concentrate to being no better than straw.

Thirdly, grass at its best from a feeding point of view is highly succulent and laxative and raises certain difficulties in feeding.

The problem of seasonal growth is one that every grassland farmer must study if he wishes to have good-quality grazing over as long a period as possible and so cheapen his feeding costs tremendously.

A considerable extension of the grazing season is possible and a more even growth of grass can be maintained throughout the season by proper use of different varieties and strains of grasses and clovers, and by correct fertiliser application at the appropriate times.

158

The guiding principles are to cut or graze grass before it passes its best feeding stage, to give it adequate rest to recover, and to maintain soil fertility by adequate applications of potash, phosphate and nitrogen at times when the root systems are best able to deal with them.

Dairy farmers who set out to establish good grass on their farms and to evolve a system of management to suit conditions and stock will be well repaid. They will be cheapening the cost of milk production and, as good leys become due for ploughing in during a rotation, they will benefit from heavier yields of crops by reason of improved fertility.

But it is just as important to make proper use of the grass as it is to plan to grow it wisely. This, too, is a subject that needs mastering if grass is to be exploited to the fullest extent.

The seasonal variation in feeding value has already been noted. Young, rapidly growing pasture has a dry-matter analysis value similar to a concentrate. Nevertheless, as a sole food for dairy cows it is deficient in fibre and too laxative. Thus the digestion of young grass is relatively inefficient.

FALL IN FEEDING VALUE

At later stages of growth there is a steady fall in feeding value and an increase in fibre content. Consequently, at the pre-flowering stage, grass has a dry-matter analysis similar to weatings, and the fibre content is at its optimum for efficient ruminant digestion.

Growth beyond the flowering stage to over-ripeness leads to a further fall in feeding value. Indeed, when much of our grass is cut for hay its feeding value, on a dry-matter basis, is less than half its value when young. Likewise the content of indigestible fibre has increased more than six times.

The level of soil fertility and the balance between grasses and legumes in the sward affects the feeding value at all these stages.

The assessment of the value of a pasture at any time needs considerable skill. Furthermore, the physical effort required of the cow in grazing must not be overlooked.

FERTILISER APPLICATION TO GRASSLAND

Modern fertiliser practice is related to the intensity of grazing, i.e. stocking rate, and the recommended rates of application per hectare. The amount of rainfall has a marked effect upon grass growth and fertiliser applications cannot be effectively used unless there is adequate moisture in the soil.

With a good type of soil it is possible to stock dairy cows (500–550 kg liveweight) at a level of 2·2 to 2·5 cows per hectare (i.e. 0·45 to 0·4 hectares per cow). To achieve this it is necessary to provide fertiliser at the level of 300–350 kg N per hectare, 40–60 kg P_2O_5 and 40–60 kg K_2O.

The actual level needs to be closely related to a soil analysis which can be carried out by ADAS or commercial firms.

The nitrogen in the spring is applied as a straight dressing, whereas phosphate and potash are applied with nitrogen during mid-season, avoiding the risk of grass staggers. This is followed by straight nitrogen if required in the late August period.

The application of fertiliser has to be planned to correspond with the feed requirements of the dairy herd for fresh grass and grass for conservation. As fertiliser prices rise so it becomes important that all the grass grown is effectively used.

Grass surplus to grazing requirement should always be cut and conserved. Ensiled grass does not deteriorate with keeping provided the clamp or silo is properly sealed.

To utilise fertiliser to the maximum, it has been thought necessary to install irrigation. This is a capital investment which has to be considered carefully. Less intensive stock rates (1·4–2·0 cows per hectare) require much less fertiliser, i.e. 200–250 kg nitrogen per hectare, and 25–30 kg of P_2O_5 and K_2O. At this level of stocking rate it is possible for clover to play a useful part in the provision of nitrogen in the sward. Production from this type of sward is low and it is much more suited to extensive grazing areas, as found in marginal areas, with thin soils.

APPLICATION OF SLURRY

Slurry varies widely in manurial value. An average analysis would be 35 kg N, 11 kg P_2O_5, 58 kg K_2O in 10 m^3 of slurry. The use of slurry tends to build up potash-rich swards. Under grazing conditions this could lead to problems of hypomagnesaemia.

Where slurry is used, fertiliser dressings can be reduced. If slurry is applied to spring-sown crops in the spring, then due account can be taken of the N, P and K levels.

In the autumn, the value of nitrogen in slurry will be much less and must not be taken into account.

SOILING OF PASTURES

This is a problem with heavy stocking. Herbage soiled by urine is not eaten by stock for 3–4 weeks, but herbage soiled by dung is unpalatable for much longer. Alternating grazing with cutting helps to maintain sward palatability, whereas zero-grazing offers an opportunity to intensify stocking rates beyond that obtainable by grazing only, and is a distinct possibility where land is highly valuable or liable to poaching by grazing stock.

CUTS DOWN PRODUCTION

Research has shown that density of the sward, its stage of growth, and the digestibility of the individual species all markedly affect the quantities actually consumed.

In twenty-four hours, a cow normally spends seven to eight hours grazing and then ceases to feed, probably from fatigue, even if the normal limit of grass consumption has not been reached.

Low-density swards with the grasses running to ear may mean that the cow is not consuming to her full capacity, with consequent limitations on her production.

Grass consumption on a young, dense sward is 68 kg DM daily, but when the same sward is 25–30 cm high consumption falls to 32 kg DM.

CONTROLLED GRAZING

The objective in controlled grazing is to raise milk output per hectare by consumption of the grass at its optimum stage of growth, with the minimum of waste. Ideally, grass should be eaten off quickly and then given a rest period of varying duration during the growing season. In practice, there are three systems which are currently used with grazed grass:

1. Strip Grazing

This type of controlled grazing was introduced into the United Kingdom as the first attempt at controlled grazing. In this system a limited grazing area is allowed each day behind an electric fence. The fence can be moved once or twice daily. The system is a most efficient means of rationing grass as the grazed area can be very strictly controlled and the grass can be eaten off as closely as desired.

The area of grass on offer each day must be closely related to the requirement of the cows and matched to the availability of the grass. If the area is too large then utilisation is poor and the cows select particular grasses. When the area is too small it is likely that a constraint will have been placed on the cows' ability to produce milk from grass. Under wet soil conditions, poaching will probably occur along the line of the fence. Recovery is likely to be slow where the stocking is too intense and the grass has been grazed too low. The system does give efficient use of grass and frees other land for conservation purposes.

If progress across a field is slow, grass at the far end of the field may well become too mature; therefore it is advisable to cut for conservation to allow a regrowth for grazing later.

Something like 0·4 hectare per day would provide grass for forty cows. This figure is only a rough guide as there are so many variables as to the amount of grass, density and height, current rainfall pattern and the level of nitrogen applied.

The system has a high labour requirement and this has accounted for its general decline in popularity.

2. Paddock Grazing

This system was introduced as an alternative to strip grazing, giving a high degree of grass utilisation without a high labour requirement. The system is based on the rotational principle of graze and rest. After being grazed off, the grass is allowed to recover with a rest period of 21–28 days, before being grazed again. After each grazing, it is important that each paddock should be top-dressed with nitrogen to help the regrowth. The amount depends upon the rest between grazings, but is usually at a level of 2·5 kg/hectare/day.

Ideally the paddocks are for one day's grazing, but this only applies for part of the season. In the mid May to early June flush it is quite likely that the paddocks would need to be subdivided, one paddock lasting two days. This intensive use of paddocks will allow grass on other paddocks to be conserved for silage in the early season.

A reasonable guide to stocking density would be one hundred cows per hectare per day. This has to be in conjunction with adequate rainfall and nitrogen top dressing. Recovery after grazing also depends upon these two factors.

As the season progresses to July, it may be that the one-day paddock is not able to supply sufficient grass. There is a modification of the system whereby the herd is split into two groups, a leader-follower system, the newly calved cows taking the best grass, followed by the low-yielders and/or dry cows.

Soiling tends to build up over the season and as rejection of grass increases it often becomes necessary to top the pastures. New growth is then encouraged.

A paddock system should be adequately watered, troughs should be placed between paddocks and there should be easy access to them. Movement to and from the paddocks is greatly helped by provision of farm roads. Ideally, a hard road is required with good access to the paddocks.

Bail milking.

Cows zero-grazing from a trailer on a Cheshire farm. This system
is expensive in equipment but it saves fencing and laying on of
water to fields.

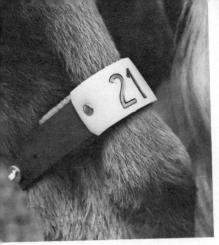

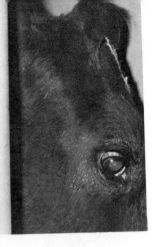

COW IDENTIFICATION

Positive cow identification is important in milking today's bigger herds. Some of the different methods in use are shown here and on the facing page.

Above: Garter type and numbered neck chain.

Below: Plastic ear tag and neck strap.

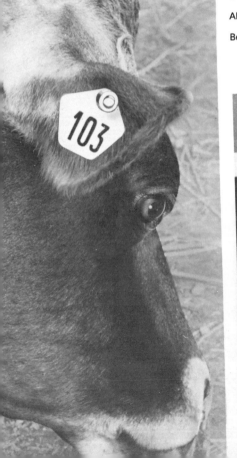

Above: Freeze brand, put on with an ultra-cold branding iron.

Right: Udder tattoo.

Below: Tail tag and anklet.

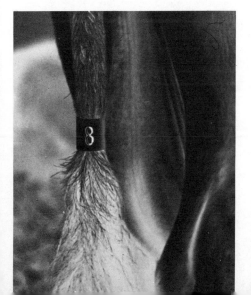

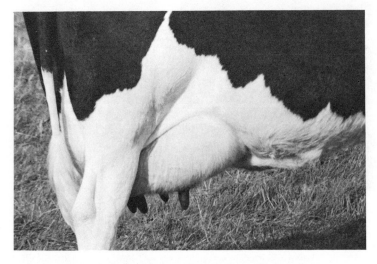

The size of the milk well, through which the large vein from the udder enters the chest wall, is an indication of a cow's yielding capacity. It should be big enough to take the tip of the third finger in most cases. The vein itself—known as the 'milk vein'—should be prominent and tortuous.

Freeze branding using irons cooled in liquid nitrogen

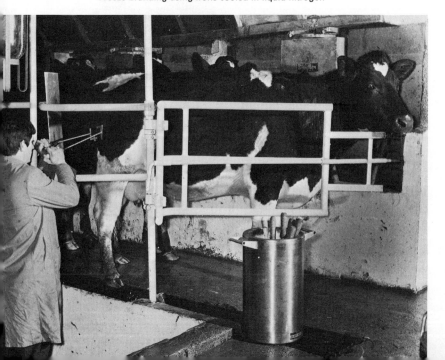

Paddock grazing did achieve widespread popularity. Most farmers appreciated the discipline of the system and also realised the advantage of its efficient grass use coupled with flexibility.

3. Set Stocking

The system of set stocking developed as an attempt to match the traditional set stocking with the tighter stocking rates of the paddock grazing system. High levels of nitrogen are applied in paddock grazing. Cows are given free access to grazing over a set area, and the fencing is removed. Stocking rates are, if anything, slightly less intensive than the paddock systems, at an average of five cows per hectare for the grazing area. Nitrogen applications are in the range of 250–350 kg/hectare; the regular application of one dressing per month (at 60 kg/hectare) eases the management aspect of the grassland.

Grazing management is very simple; cows are turned out when the grass is very short and the normal winter rations are continued. As the grass grows so the other foods are reduced and then stopped. With all the set stocked area available, the cows do not poach the grass in wet weather. As the season progresses, the grazing area should be increased, starting at 0·16 hectare/cow and increasing to 0·22 hectare/cow by July/August. Silage aftermaths can be included in the system. There is a marked difference in the sward between the more open type to be found on the paddock system and the dense sward of the set system.

With the close grazing, clover is more likely to be present; the dense sward also discourages the ingress of weed grasses.

The main reason for the popularity of the set stocking system is the simplicity of management; a practical criticism is that it takes longer to collect the dairy herd from a large set stocked area at milking time. On many farms the area is divided into two, a day and a night pasture; this may fit certain farm layouts.

The milk production on each of the systems mentioned is very similar. The reasons for a farmer adopting any one of the systems is more likely to be related to layout of the farm, soil type and the personal preference of the farmer.

VALUE OF WILTING

The problem of ensuring that cows obtain highly nutritive grass and, at the same time, eat enough fibre and dry matter is a real one.

Young, dense swards have a high moisture content. The water in and on the grass may approach 90 per cent of its weight, and the dry-matter consumption of a cow grazing it will be less than if she eats air-dry foods.

For this reason the late Professor Boutflour suggested mowing such grass and allowing it to wilt before grazing. This practice increases the dry-matter consumption of the cows; it is also worthwhile as a preventative of bloat. I have employed it successfully with high-yielding cows.

SUPPLEMENTARY FEEDING OF COWS AT GRASS

The production of milk that can be expected from grass is dependent on the value of the grass and the quantity of grass available.

The value of the grass is best assessed using the 'D' value rating. This 'D' value is determined by variety, stage of growth, fertiliser treatment and the season.

In the early grazing season, 'D' values are rated at 70 plus; by June/July, the value has dropped to 65–70, and during August there is a further drop to 60–65.

The quality of grass available at any time is a result of season, the current weather pattern and the level of fertiliser application. General patterns of grass growth are widely accepted but there is considerable variation between the seasons; long-term planning over a season for grass growth can prove to be very difficult.

In the early part of the season, supplementary feeding is largely unnecessary, except in the case of the high-yielding cow (25–30 litres) which can only be expected to take 10–15 litres from grass, otherwise she will drop in milk yield and lose body condition.

With lower-yielding cows, supplementary feeding would tend to reduce grass consumption and be less profitable. In the case of high-yielding cows, it may be considered where the maintenance of a high-energy diet is important in respect of both yield and compositional quality of milk.

Supplementary feeds for the high-yield cows should be those high in energy such as barley, sugar beet pulp nuts, etc.

By mid-season July/August the potential of grass falls considerably. This is the time when silage aftermaths can be brought in; also the spring re-seeds can play a part.

MANAGEMENT AT 'TURN-OUT'

It can be realised, therefore, that supplementary feeding of protein, under spring and early summer grazing conditions in this country, is largely unnecessary. The feeding of cows at grass—except during periods of drought—is largely a question of supplying supplements of high-energy value.

To counteract the laxative nature of young grass and to mitigate the risk of bloat, the changeover from winter feed to summer grazing should be made gradually. In the earliest stages of growth—probably from early to late April—the cows should continue to receive a feed of roughage before they go out to grass in the morning.

An electric fence enables the grass to be rationed; where strip-grazing is not used, the cows should be allowed up to one and a half hours' grazing after the evening milking and then returned to a bare lie-back field for the night.

Once the grass has lost its laxative character, the feeding of roughage can cease.

If 3 kg or so of roughage are allowed per cow per day, then one hour's grazing will be required to meet maintenance needs and an additional hour's grazing will be required for each 5·0 kg milk produced up to 15·0 kg. Where an electric fence is being used it should be adjusted to enclose an area which is large enough to allow this time being spent in continuous grazing without leaving surplus herbage.

By the time the grass reaches the pre-flowering stage (20–25 cm long) most cows can be allowed to consume grass to appetite. Those yielding over 20 litres should continue to be rationed with grass and they should receive some supplementary feeding of concentrated foods.

It is instructive to point out at this stage that the extent of the rise in milk yield experienced when the cows first go out to grass is an indication of the inadequacy and quality of the home-grown foods fed in late winter.

Under good management, where high-quality home-grown foods have been available in adequate supply, the rise should not exceed 10 per cent in total milk yield. If greater than this in spite of good management, then better quality home-grown foods are necessary.

GUIDE TO SUMMER FEEDING

As a practical guide to the summer feeding of dairy cows, the following scheme is suggested, bearing in mind the need for adjusting the grass consumption per cow by increasing the area grazed or the time allowed for grazing, according to the rate of decline recorded in milk yields.

The feeding of some roughage, as when cows are on young, highly nutritive pasture, is also commendable in its effect on

Table 11.1 Summer Feeding

Time of year	Growth stage of grass	Roughage	Concentrates for production
Early spring (April)	10–15 cm, young and leafy (grazing controlled 4 hours daily)	hay (3·2 kg)	* cereals at 0·4 kg per kg over 13·6 kg
Early summer (May)	20–25 cm, pre-flowering stage (grazing to appetite)	none	* cereals at 0·4 kg per kg over 18·1 kg
Summer (June)	flowering stage (grazing to appetite)	none	balanced concentrates for yields over 13·6 kg
Mid summer (July)	flowering stage (grazing to appetite)	none	balanced concentrates for yields over 9·1 kg
Late summer (August)	aftermath or green fodder in times of drought. (grazing to appetite)	none	balanced concentrates for yields over 4·5 kg
Early autumn (September)	young aftermath or maiden seeds (grazing to appetite)	3·2 kg hay or 12·7 kg kale or green catch crops	balanced concentrates for yields over 9·1 kg

* Mineral mixture added supplying the necessary magnesium supplement.

maintaining the butterfat percentage in milk. This often shows a marked decline in the early part of the grazing season.

DROUGHT SAFEGUARDS

When pastures fail during drought conditions, the supplementary feeding of cows will have to be on a much more liberal scale if milk yields are to be maintained. Silage offers an excellent standby in this respect, so does lucerne which can be grazed quite well behind an electric fence. If bloat is feared, the crop should be mown and wilted twenty-four hours before grazing. Another possibility is irrigation. However, the capital cost of this exercise has become excessive if used only for the dairy herd. If an arable interest can also be served, e.g. potatoes, then the cost is spread and the project is likely to be more viable.

THE VALUE OF AUTUMN GRASS

The milk-producing value of autumn grazing is, except for maiden seeds sown the same year, below that of similar grass in the spring flush.

This lower feeding value is generally appreciated by stockmen, but the scientific explanation is less clear. I believe that the higher fibre content of autumn grass, despite its high protein analysis, is one of the possible reasons, together with lower sugar content.

In practice, the production value of autumn grass is at least nine litres per cow less per day than similar grazing in spring. Failure to appreciate this fact will lead the dairyman to be too late in providing extra supplementary food for the cows and heifers, and is often the explanation of a catastrophic fall in the milk yield of cows in early winter, particularly after a flush of autumn grass.

It is fatally easy to over-estimate the value of autumn grass to incalf heifers and heavy-milking cows and so to cause a drop in their production which cannot be regained.

There seems to be a definite advantage in maiden seeds for autumn grazing. They appear to have a higher milk-producing value than older leys or permanent pasture, and where it is possible to have a small acreage available each year in the course of the rotation, it will prove particularly valuable for this purpose.

Other supplementary grazing crops will also be useful at this time of year. Those usually grown are rape, kale and ryegrass and trefoil mixtures. Assuming that the pasture being grazed provides for maintenance purposes, which is probably true in most parts of the country until late September, about 12·7 kg of one of these green crops will provide for 4·5 litres of milk.

ELECTRIC FENCING GUIDE

Some practical points in the use of electric fences are worth emphasis:

1. Follow the maker's instructions carefully in erection. Ensure a tight wire, effectively insulated and free of any possible earthing by contact with the crop being folded off.

2. Run the fence so as to include a water trough, or access to the trough from the area being grazed. Particularly on rape or kale, cattle show a marked desire to drink before the appetite level of consumption is reached.

3. Allow sufficient frontage or feeding space per cow. Two metres of wire per cow is, in my experience, sufficient.

4. Calculating the area allowed per cow on that basis, Table 11.2 has been compiled to show the area of the fold per cow per day, with varying levels of consumption.

To estimate yield per hectare: In metric terms, weigh the crop

Table 11.2. Hectares per Cow According to Yield of Grass per Hectare and Level of Production per Cow

Yield per hectare (tonne)	M + 5 kg	M + 10 kg	M + 15 kg	M + 20 kg
10	1/300	1/250	1/200	1/150
20	1/600	1/500	1/400	1/300

over an average square metre in kilograms; dividing by ten will give the yield in tonnes per hectare.

Where conditions are very wet underfoot this margin for waste should be increased, particularly with kale, as the cows usually bite off the tops and eat them on the ground.

5. In grazing large fields of grass, where the time required to graze the whole area will exceed a week, it is advisable to use a back fence. This prevents defoliating the sward as it recovers from the previous grazing.

In this chapter, the importance of good management in the utilisation of the increased productivity from new leys has been stressed.

RELATING GRASS TO MILK

The only way in which the profitable relationship between grass production and milk yields can be established is to record the output of milk and to relate it closely to the amount of grass available. When cows go out to spring grass after the acclimatisation period, it is then likely that by mid-May the grass will supply most of what the cow needs in the way of energy and protein. Mention has been made of the possibility of expecting too much from the grass. However, the problem tends to occur in late July when the grass supply becomes short in either quality, quantity or both. The question of supplementation then becomes a management question. If the yield starts to decline at a rate greater than the normal, the question is what will it cost to reduce the rate of milk decline. The problem is solved by feeding supplements to one group of cows to see if the milk can be stabilised. A simple comparison of cost of feed against value of milk recovered will provide an answer. If twenty pence was required to regain milk to the value of twenty-five pence, the cost benefit is not too clear-cut. However, the other factor to be taken into account is the level of milk yield likely through the remainder of the grass season, with the possibility

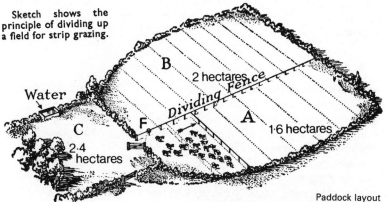

Sketch shows the principle of dividing up a field for strip grazing.

Paddock layout for 42 cows, taken from the ICI booklet 'Paddock Grazing' allowing one day's grazing per 0·4 hectare paddock and three-weekly circulation.

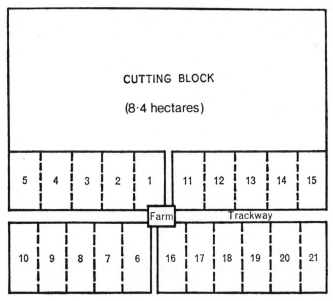

0·4 Hectare Paddock

of an autumn flush of grass. A higher milk yield from supplemented cows would then be obtained wholly from bulk feed. This approach puts the issue of supplementary feeding into the category of a management decision, rather than one simply concerned with nutrition.

THE LARGE HERD AT GRASS

With the general increase in the size of herds, the question of farm layout to facilitate movement of cows to and from pasture requires careful consideration. Access to paddocks is best provided from a central 'race' with wide gates opening across the race to control the herd and reduce poaching.

Herds of over one hundred cows are difficult to accommodate as one herd under grazing conditions. The set stocking systems tend to deal with some of the problems such as poaching. On the paddock system the solution is to divide the herd in two groups, possibly high- and low-yield. The nutritional requirements of the groups are different; mention has been made of the leader–follower system which has been used successfully in many cases.

It is possible then for the large dairy herd to be more efficient at utilising grassland; it offers the possibility of grouping cows at grass, a system which would be impracticable with a small herd.

CHAPTER 12

MODERN MILKING TECHNIQUES

BEFORE the principles of efficient milking can be fully appreciated, it should be explained that the udder of the cow is composed of four quarters, each separately constituted and supported by strong ligaments—the median and lateral suspensory ligaments.

Each quarter is composed of secretory tissue in which the milk is made from constituents carried to the cells of the alveoli by the blood stream.

MILK SECRETION CELLS

UDDER CISTERN

COLLECTION SPACE

Cross-section of udder.   Secretory tissue.   Cross-section of alveolus.

From these cells the milk drains by the milk ducts to the milk cistern located above each teat. This cistern varies in capacity with individual cows but will normally hold about one pint of milk. It opens through a circular fold of tissue into the teat which is closed at its apex by strong sphincter muscles around the teat opening or orifice.

When milk is expressed by squeezing the teat from above downwards, the circular fold of tissue at the top of the teat is closed, thus shutting off the canal from the milk cistern and forcing the milk in the teat canal through the teat opening. When pressure is relaxed the teat canal refills with milk.

Points of a Good Udder

The cow's udder should be silky to the touch and free from any hard areas which are often the result of mastitis.

The veins which leave the fore part of the udder and extend along the abdomen should be well developed; the size of the 'milk well' through which the large vein enters the chest wall should be capacious—in most cows it will accommodate the tip of the third finger and is, anatomically, one of the best indications of a cow's yielding capacity.

The udder should hang as level as possible, but in aged cows becomes increasingly pendulous as the supporting ligaments weaken, and the hind-quarters invariably hang lower than the fore-quarters, mainly due to the fact that, as a general rule, more milk is given by the hind- than the fore-quarters.

Commonly quoted figures are that 55 per cent of the milk is given by the hind-quarters and 45 per cent by the fore-quarters. This physiological variation presents a problem in machine milking where, theoretically, all the teat cups should be removed immediately milking has finished. The objective of all breeders should be to produce dairy cows which possess evenly balanced udders well suited to machine milking.

Preserving Udder Shape

The actual formation of milk in the udder requires approximately 1800 litres of blood to circulate through the gland to make 4·5 litres of milk. From this it can be realised how great a strain lactation imposes on the circulatory system and consequently how vital it is for heavy-yielding cows to be treated quietly, handled gently, and allowed adequate periods of rest.

They should never be driven rapidly with full udders, nor walked long distances, if udder shape and attachment are to be preserved.

When Milk is Reabsorbed

Research by Petersen and his colleagues in the USA has shown that milk secretion is a continuous process that goes on steadily between milkings unless the accumulation of milk sets up an internal udder pressure. When this pressure reaches from thirty to forty millimetres of mercury in the alveoli cells further secretion is prevented and the milk constituents begin to be reabsorbed into the bloodstream.

With cows in early lactation this is likely to occur about nine hours after milking. Hence the advisability of milking heavy-yielding cows more than twice daily.

The initiation of milk secretion at calving, or before, is due to the release of hormones into the bloodstream. Two hormones are involved: prolactin from the pituitary gland and thyroxine from the thyroid gland.

THE 'LET-DOWN' OF MILK

The actual 'let-down' of milk at milking time is also controlled by a hormone known as oxytocin which is released into the blood stream by the pituitary gland when the cow is stimulated by suckling, washing or handling of the teats.

The effect of this hormone is to cause a contraction of muscular tissue around the milk cells so that milk is released into the milk cistern and teats. The turgidity of the teats is a physical sign that the let-down phenomenon has occurred.

Once the let-down mechanism has been properly stimulated the release of milk is rapid, and if milking is then carried out quickly, the evacuation of the udder is effective. Conversely if the let-down mechanism is incomplete, or if it is exhausted before milking is finished—this could occur if milking took longer than eight to ten minutes—the evacuation of milk is inefficient no matter what pressure is applied to the teats.

Interference with normal let-down occurs if the cow is either upset or excited; the phenomenon works to its fullest extent when the cow is happy, contented and accustomed to a regular milking routine.

FOUR BASIC PRINCIPLES

These facts form the basis of the milking management recommended below:

1. The cows must be ready for milking and not nervous or excited, either by strange surroundings or unusual noises.

2. Stimulate the udder and teats by washing in warm water—as is normal in any clean milk production routine.

3. Apply teat cups within two minutes of washing.

4. Once milking has begun, milk as rapidly and quietly as possible.

THE MILKING MACHINE

A simple description of how the milking machine functions and its basic components will provide a useful prelude to considering

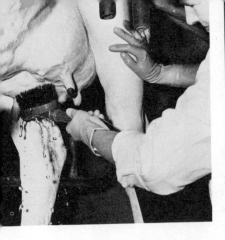

Udder and teats should be washed with warm water not more than three minutes before teat cups are applied.

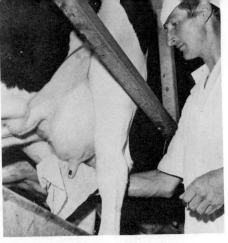

Wiping and drying the udder with paper towel soaked with disinfectant.

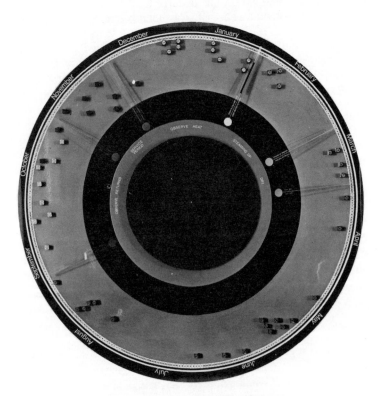

A breeding chart such as this can be fixed on the parlour wall or in the farm office and will provide at-a-glance details of how long each animal has been calved, when it is due for service, when it was confirmed in calf, when it should be dried off and steamed up, etc. Each cow is represented by a numbered magnetic cube.

its possible contribution to the spread of infection. The milking machine works on the principle of encouraging milk flow by reducing the pressure outside the teat to half that of atmospheric pressure.

The required capacity of the pump to extract air is determined by the number of milking units used. Practice has shown that the most suitable vacuum for efficient milk extraction is 38 cm mercury. To maintain this level, a controller is fitted to a galvanised iron pipe connecting the vacuum pump to the milking units. When the pressure exceeds 38 cm the weight is lifted off its seating and the pressure restored to the necessary level; the pressure is approximately 33 cm mercury at the teat cup.

The pulsator mechanism supplies air and vacuum alternately to the cavity between the metal cup and the liner. This causes the liner to collapse and open at regular intervals, and provides the regular relief for the teats. The number of times that the liner opens and closes each minute is referred to as the pulse rate and is normally in the range of fifty to sixty.

The period for which it remains in the open or closed position is known as the pulsation ratio and can vary with different makes of machine from 1:1 to 3:1.

Milk from the teat cups is led via short milk tubes into the small collection chamber or claw piece where it enters the long milk tube and via measuring jars and pipes, empties ultimately in a glass receiver jar. From here it is extracted by a rotary pump and discharged at atmospheric pressure into a bulk storage tank. For the milk to flow freely from the teat cups and milk tubes it is essential for the claw piece to have an air admission hole.

A milking machine which is wrongly designed, worn or badly maintained can present many risks to udder health.

MASTITIS CONTROL

To control mastitis, strict hygiene and good machine milking techniques are necessary. Mastitis is an inflammation of the udder caused mainly by bacterial infection. Bacteria enter the udder by way of the teat duct and are spread at milking from infected udders or teat sores, via the milking equipment. There are two main types of bacteria involved: streptococcal and staphylococcal, accounting for some 90 per cent of mastitis cases.

Mastitis can be present in the udder at varying levels, described as:

(a) sub-clinical mastitis—where the udder and milk appear

normal but infection is present, milk yield and quality are
reduced.
(b) clinical mastitis. In this case there are obvious symptoms of
inflammation, e.g. swollen quarters and/or clots in the milk.

Detection of Mastitis

It would be difficult to detect infection in individual cows at the
sub-clinical level. Control is achieved by examining the cell count
of a bulk milk sample from the herd. This is done on a monthly
basis by the appropriate Marketing Board. In England and Wales,
the samples are cell counted at the laboratories at Worcester.

Herds with an average bulk milk cell count of less than 500,000
cells/ml usually have little trouble from udder disease while cell
counts in excess of a million normally indicate a high level of
infection. A reasonable cell count to aim for would be 250,000.
Mastitis cannot be eradicated so it is essential to contain it at a
reasonable level.

In addition to the monthly samples taken by the Board there is
available a whole range of Board services concerned with the
monitoring of mastitis. Individual samples from cows can be tested
and advisory visits can be made by Board staff. The local veterinary
surgeon should be aware of the cell count level in any herd and
be informed of any increase in this level.

Control of Infection

The strategy for mastitis control is to:

1. Eliminate existing udder infections

(a) by milking and self-cure processes:

- Quite a number of infections of the sub-clinical type disappear.
  The mechanical removal of milk helps in this, also the host
  defence mechanisms.
- Vaccination. This has not yet been established as a commercial
  possibility, but is being investigated.
- Cull the persistent offenders. They are dangerous to keep in
  the herd because of high risk of transfer of infection. As a
  general rule, cows which fail to respond to three courses of
  treatment in one quarter in one lactation are incurable and
  should be culled.

(b) by therapy: This can be tackled in two stages. With in-milk
cows, a blitz can be carried out by treating all four quarters of
infected cows with a course of antibiotics. The next stage is to
submit all cows to a dry cow therapy course of treatment. This

involves treating all quarters of all cows with antibiotics at drying off time. The treatment is a most important feature of controlling summer mastitis (August bag). A careful watch on all in-calf and dry cattle during the mid/late summer is essential.

2. The prevention of new udder infection. Before milking, there must be adequate preparation of the cow by washing and drying the udder. This should remove all the dirt attached to the udder. It is preferable to use a hose with warm water, containing a suitable iodophor or hypochlorite for this purpose. Paper towels and rubber gloves should be used. Udder cloths should not be used; they become very contaminated and therefore an extremely dangerous source of infection.

After washing and drying, the fore milk should be taken. This allows milk from each quarter to be examined in turn so that infected quarters can be identified. Milk from infected quarters must be discarded for the period recommended by the manufacturer.

Ideally, the order of milking should be heifers, milk cows and lastly any infected animals. This is not always practicable.

After milking, the teats should be dipped in one of the commercially available teat dips. The dilution of the teat dip must be in strict accordance with the manufacturer's instructions.

Recent developments have included the introduction of sprays for the teats but this does not seem to be as effective as the teat dip system. If there are problems with teat sores or chaps, teat dips with lanolin or glycerin should be used.

3. Mastitis and machine milking. The milking machine can be a cause of mastitis if it is inefficiently operated. Every milking set-up should be checked regularly; the main features to be tested include vacuum pumps, controllers, air bleeds, level of vacuum, pulsation rates and liners.

The MMB offer a Milking Machine Testing Service, which provides visits to farms by a trained MMB fieldsman who will complete a comprehensive report on the state of the milking machine, and can correct many of the more common faults at the time of the test. The charge (until April 1982) in England and Wales is £22.30 for a plant of up to six units, plus £1.10 for each additional unit.

4. Mastitis, housing and management. To prevent mastitis the dairyman must minimise the conditions under which bacteria thrive and multiply. This means paying attention to 'dry, clean cubicle

Sketch on left shows normal action of teat–cups: right-hand sketch shows harmful effect on lining of teats when cups " creep " up.

beds. Dimensions of the cubicle and the slope of the bed are critical factors in providing conditions which will keep the udder clean. Loafing areas and collecting yards should be kept clean. Where feet, legs and ends of tails become coated with slurry, so the incidence of disease is likely to increase.

Dung passages should be scraped twice daily if possible, with particular attention being paid to the edges of the cubicle. There should be adequate floor space for each cow and adequate drainage. Fly control is important; also the ends of tails can be clipped to limit contamination.

The overall need is to provide clean, dry housing conditions for the dairy cow which will ultimately be reflected in the improved quality of the milk produced.

Mastitis is a costly disease to farmers, taking some £20 million per year—hence the need to control it effectively.

A disturbing trend that has recently come to light is that as modern long-acting antibiotics so effectively sterilise the udder as part of mastitis control, so the cows in fact become more prone, in winter, to environmental (*E. coli*) mastitis immediately after calving.

MILKING THREE TIMES DAILY

The reabsorption of milk and cessation of secretion, which occurs when the milk pressure in the udder reaches about 25 per cent above normal blood pressure, has already been noted. This re-exchange of milk constituents (particularly of milk sugar) with the bloodstream appears to have the effect of discouraging further secretion and so sets in motion the drying off processes in the udder. Therefore, milking more frequently not only ensures continual secretion, but also postpones decline in lactation or drying off.

Milking more than twice a day is, fundamentally, an economic problem. It requires shift systems of labour, but nevertheless, with potentially high-yielding cows it will raise lactation yields by ten to fifteen per cent.

When it Pays

It is not uncommon now for cows to give more than twenty litres of milk at any one milking. Cows capable of this will undoubtedly show an increase in milk yield by three-times milking, an increase which should repay the extra feed and labour cost.

Three-times milking has the advantage of reducing the milk load in the udder and so lessening the tendency for it to become pendulous because of the increased strain on the suspensory ligaments.

Maximum production from high-yielding cows will only be obtained where three-times milking is practised. The next best thing is to milk as nearly as possible at twelve-hour intervals; the third best practice is to milk the highest-yielders first at the morning milking and last at the evening milking—this helps to space out the milking times without making the dairyman's day unduly long. However, herd averages of 7000+ litres per cow have been achieved on twice-a-day milking.

How Long to Keep it up

It should be emphasised that the loss of milk yield resulting directly from undue pressure is most marked in the first three months of a cow's lactation. Later in the lactation—when the volume of milk secreted is less while the storage capacity of the udder remains unchanged—twice-daily milking will give results nearly comparable with thrice-daily milking.

The change from thrice-daily milking to twice-daily milking can be made without any drastic reduction in yield when a cow's daily yield has fallen to two-thirds of the peak yield.

However, should the twice-daily milking intervals be grossly unequal—e.g. sixteen hours and eight hours—the effect of the change would be most marked. In fact, where more equal intervals than this are impossible on twice-daily milking, it would be better to continue three-times milking until the yield is down to about one-half of the recorded peak.

RECORDING IS ESSENTIAL

Official milk recording in the United Kingdom is organised by the Milk Marketing Board in England and Wales; in Scotland by the Scottish Milk Records Association, and in Northern Ireland by the Ministry of Agriculture. The objectives of milk recording are as follows.

1. It provides a guide in the management of cows whereby accurate feeding according to yield can be carried out.

2. Milk yields are a check on the health of the cow as well as on managerial factors such as feeding and milking routine.

3. Official milk records and butterfat testing are the means of assessing the productive ability of breeding stock and give the information needed in the breeding of better dairy cattle.

4. Milk records are an important factor in the sales of pedigree stock, particularly bulls.

Under good management where feeding, milking and general welfare of the cattle are satisfactory, a study of the milk records provides a background against which errors and mistakes in management can be detected. When the recorded milk yields of cows are plotted on a graph week by week, a composite lactation curve can be drawn which typifies the milking performance of the average cow in the herd.

WHAT A LACTATION CURVE SHOWS

Such a curve, drawn from milk-yield data, indicates the following general features.

1. After calving, a cow's milk yield will rise steadily for a period of from four to ten weeks when the yield reaches its peak. The time taken for the cow to reach its peak is very much associated with the level of feeding.

It must be appreciated that thanks to the use of AI the national dairy herd is now very well bred. The question of milk yield and peak is a matter of exploring the milk yield potential of the cow. Heavier levels of feeding will produce higher yields of milk, and a longer time taken to attain peak yield. An important management task is to decide what level of yield is required on a particular farm. In an intensive farm with limited land, a high peak yield of thirty litres (e.g. 6000 litres annual average) attained at six to ten weeks is required, which may have to be largely obtained from bought-in concentrates and bulk feeds.

In an extensive farm where land is not a limiting factor, the maximum of quality home-grown foods will be produced and utilised for milk production. Lower peak yields (20–25 litres) will lead to lactation yields of 5000 litres or less which will be more quickly attained during the post-calving period at perhaps four to six weeks.

2. The daily peak of heifers is approximately 1/220 of the official 305-day lactation yield and 1/200 in the case of older cows. The objective is to make the best possible profit from the combination

of level of milk produced and the cost of food required to produce the milk. This can be simply stated:

Profit = margin per litre × number of litres produces.

Where there is ample home-grown bulk food of good quality then the equation should read:

(a) Profit = a large margin per litre × a small number of litres.

If in another situation there is a shortage of quality home-grown bulk food, then to attain a profit similar to (a) the alternative has to be:

(b) Profit = a small margin per litre × a large number of litres.

The two expressions show the limits between which any dairy herd must be managed.

The question as to whether a low input or high input can be practised is to be related basically to the farming system.

The regular monitoring of yield and feed input is the only way in which an attempt can be made to correlate these two factors which largely govern the profitability of any dairy farm.

Intelligent use of milk records is thus not only an index of milk yield but also reflects the management of the herd as a whole.

Thus—a heifer giving 20 litres per day at her peak should produce a lactation yield of 4400 litres and a cow peaking at 27 litres per day at her peak should produce a lactation yield of 5400 litres.

3. Once the peak yield has been reached, the subsequent decline in yield is at the rate of approximately 2·5 per cent per week or 10 per cent per month.

Heifers do not attain peak yields as high as cows; they also tend to hold the yield at this lower level for a longer period and do not decline at the same rate as the average cow.

Milk Yield and Feeding

A more rapid decline than the 2·5 per cent mentioned would indicate underfeeding. It is important to feed a cow well in early lactation to allow her to perform three important functions. They are:

● To attain a peak yield which is required by management.
● To minimise body weight loss.
● To conceive if possible to first service to ensure a good calving interval.

The level of feeding during middle and late lactation has to be decided individually for each farm system.

England and Wales

National Milk Records (NMR) is the officially recognised scheme under which all records are fully authenticated and presented to the producer on a computer statement. The system involves a visit by the Board's contracted recorder once a month when the evening and morning milkings are measured and a milk sample is taken for each cow. The recorder will note the service and calving dates for each cow and details of any animal entering or leaving the herd. A copy of the recorded yields is left on the farm and the sample is sent away to the laboratories to be tested for butterfat and protein. The producer receives a full statement later giving updated yields and the quality test levels, together with a lactation certificate for any cow that has completed a full 305-day lactation during the month prior to the recording. Further information provided includes a management action list which reminds the farmer which cows which are due for service, pregnancy diagnosis, to dry off or to calve. An annual summary of the herd's completed lactations within the year October–September is supplied with details of average lactations based on these results. A more recent introduction has been the cow indexing system. The aim of this system is to rank cows within the herd on their yield of fat plus protein adjusted to a heifer equivalent basis.

The basic monthly fees are assessed on the average number of animals in the herd and range from £13·75 for a herd of one to twenty-five cows to £57·85 for one over 350 cows (Prices as at 1 April 1981.)

Scotland

The Scottish system is based on a regular monthly statement and is similar to that of England and Wales. Lactation certificates are issued for each cow on completion of the lactation and an annual statement gives details of all the lactations completed in the year.

From October 1977, the service was extended to include computer documentation including 305-day and the next-test yield projection. Production indices and calving interval figures are also available. From April 1981 a standard charge of £4·50 per lactation was made. In the north of Scotland the fee was £5·10.

Since June 1981 an optional extra cow package has been a feature of the Scottish system.

Northern Ireland

In September 1978 a computerised milk recording system was introduced by the Ministry of Agriculture, with all weighing and sampling to be carried out by board officers at monthly intervals.

Butterfat protein levels are recorded and lactation certificates are provided similar to the other schemes. There is a herd fee of £60 and a lactation fee of £6·85 per cow (1 April 1981).

INTERPRETATION OF MILK RECORDS

It must be understood that a milk record is by no means a statement of the production of which a cow is capable. It simply indicates the amount of milk she gave under a certain set of conditions.

From large numbers of records it is possible to determine several factors that act as a guide to interpreting records clearly and are an aid in improving management.

1. Age at calving. Milk yields rise with age up to the optimum at the fifth or sixth lactation and then decline with increasing age. In classifying yields as an indication of merit, breed societies take this fact into account.

2. Previous dry period. A very short dry period tends to depress the following lactation yield. The optimum dry period would appear to be about fifty to sixty days. A longer dry period may give a higher subsequent lactation yield but one not sufficiently large to offset the loss of milk from the longer dry period.

3. Service period. To calve regularly at twelve-monthly intervals a cow needs to be in-calf by the twelfth week after calving. To delay service beyond this period means a higher lactation yield but a wider calving interval, whereas earlier service could mean a lower lactation yield and a calving interval of less than a year.

4. Season of calving. Most dairy farmers would hold the opinion that autumn-calving cows give more milk than spring or summer calvers. It has been suggested that there is an 11 per cent difference in favour of October calving compared with June calving. Better cow management during the grazing season, and the use of higher-quality home-grown foods in winter feeding might significantly reduce this difference.

5. Frequency of milking. Twice-daily milking is most common, but an increase of production can be expected where:

(a) milking intervals are evenly spaced, i.e. 12-hourly intervals instead of, say 14 hours and 10 hours, particularly with cows at the height of their production;

(b) by further removing the depressing effect of udder pressure on yield, three-times milking can be expected to raise production above twice-daily milking by 10 to 15 per cent, particularly with high-yielders and potentially high-yielders, provided that no milking interval exceeds nine hours.

In interpreting official records all these factors are taken into account, and a common basis can be determined mathematically by appropriate correction factors. But for practical breeding work the important matters to bear in mind when assessing the value of a record are correction for age, service period and frequency of milking.

CHAPTER 13

SOME PROBLEMS IN MILK PRODUCTION

UP to 1975, the milk sold in England and Wales was required to have an analysis of above 3·0 per cent butterfat and 8·5 per cent solids-not-fat. As from 1 October 1976, within the framework of the EEC regulations, the United Kingdom chose to market non-standardised whole milk to the consumer of liquid milk for which the Regulation prescribes a minimum butterfat content of 3·0 per cent, but no minimum for the solids-not-fat. Since the Regulation leaves Member States free to determine the compositional standards for raw milk, the existing United Kingdom requirement of a minimum solids-not-fat content of 8·5 per cent for premium milk continues. The various quality milk schemes giving bands for payment and the possible penalties have been described in Chapter 1.

LOW BUTTERFAT

Dealing with butterfat problems first, the following possibilities arise:

Breeding. The butterfat percentage of milk varies as much between individuals of the same breed as it does betwen breeds. The production of butterfat is an inherent characteristic, so that low butterfat may be due to the breeding of cows.

The average yield and butterfat percentage in the milk of the different breeds of recorded dairy cattle in this country, as published by National Milk Records, is given in Appendix I.

Stage of lactation. During lactation, butterfat percentage falls as yield rises. Consequently, the bulked milk of a herd is more likely to fall below standard if there are, at any one time, a majority of the cows at the peak of their yields.

189

Age of cow. A high proportion of old cows in the herd will tend to reduce the butterfat in the bulk sample as the percentage of butterfat generally declines with age. Heifers test higher than cows.

Feeding. It is generally accepted that changes in feeding, on an adequate and well-balanced diet, have only a minor and temporary effect on butterfat percentage. Certain foods like palm kernel cake or coconut cake tend to raise the percentage slightly, whereas other foods—for example, cod liver oil if fed over 56 g a day—will depress it.

A cow calving in good condition will give milk of higher butterfat percentage than if she calves very lean. On an inadequate diet, yield and butterfat tend to fall below normal.

On a highly laxative diet the butterfat percentage tends to fall. This often occurs in the spring when the cows go to grass. It can be remedied by:

● restricting the intake of grass by controlled grazing, or by turning the cows on to a more mature type of pasture;
● feeding some dry roughage food such as hay or straw, say 1·8–2·7 kg daily, before the cows go to grass in the morning. I have used this method for several years with high-yielding cows.

Low butterfat may be due to a low intake of fibre; this would be most likely to happen on young spring grass.

Frequency of milking. Theoretically it is advisable to milk cows at a twelve-hour interval; in practice this is a system which is seldom adopted. With the normal period of ten to fourteen hours, the recorder is likely to find a higher butterfat level at morning milking than at the evening milking. Differences of up to 1·0 per cent have been recorded. With thrice-daily milking, milk yield is increased by up to 15 per cent. Butterfat percentage is slightly lower but can give an overall greater weight of fat.

Health and Welfare of the Cow. Cows that are off-feed or sick show a greater drop in milk yield than in butterfat percentage. Lack of exercise will also reduce butterfat percentage, as would undue excitement at milking time.

REMEDIES FOR LOW BUTTERFAT

The dairy farmer who meets the problem of low butterfat percentages has several lines of investigation to follow in tracking down the cause.

He should see that the cows calve down in good condition and are adequately fed without any tendency to scour. There should be adequate provision for exercise. Cows should be well housed. The bulking of milk in the tank averages the effect of milking interval. The provision of roughage—fibre—to the cow when on spring grass is important.

With an autumn-calving herd, higher yields, coupled with a high level of feeding can cause low butterfats. This is largely due to traditional twice-daily feeding of concentrates in the parlour, which tends to make the pH of the rumen fluctuate. At a low pH the acidity of the rumen considerably reduces the production of acetic acid which is important for the production of butterfat. The solution is to move towards multi-feeds of concentrates on a feed fence, coupled with an increase of fibre in the diets. The complete feed system also tends to satisfy some of these requirements.

If these measures fail to meet the situation, the problem is then likely to be associated with breeding. The routine monthly testing of butterfat will identify those animals which provide a constant problem. The programme for culling in the herd should eventually correct the faults but care will have to be taken in the selection of future bulls. These should be chosen for their ability to pass on better levels of butterfat production.

CAUSES OF LOW SOLIDS-NOT-FAT

The main causes of low solids-not-fat are related to the management of the herd, rather than to the breeding. The average of the breed types do show a basic difference, e.g. Ayrshires tend to have a better figure for snf and butterfat than Friesians, but feeding and management seem to largely dictate the actual levels.

Underfeeding, either in quantity or quality, for any long period, causes a significant decline in solids-not-fat in many herds. This is most likely to occur in the late winter months when fodder stocks may be running low; it will also occur if the quality of the fodder is of poor quality as a result of a bad weather at harvest time.

There is a similar danger in periods of drought; the cows may be underfed at pasture, so supplementary feeding should be introduced at the right time.

A study of snf analyses indicates that there is a definite seasonal pattern.

Snf levels are usually quite low in the late winter but rise to a peak in May and June. The level is also related to the stage of lactation. In early lactation and high milk yields, both snf and butterfat tend to be minimal, but levels rise as the lactation progresses, the snf level certainly improving as the cows move on to spring grass.

The variations in level are magnified when a herd calves on a 'block' basis; on the other hand if the herd calves over a long period of time the level of snf tends to be stabilised.

It cannot be too strongly emphasised that adequate feeding of dairy cows is essential if the quality of milk is to be maintained.

A common mistake made by too many milk producers is to delay the supplementary feeding when cows are on autumn grazing. Early autumn- and winter-calvers need special attention at this time; if they lose condition too rapidly before the onset of winter trouble can be expected the following spring.

Mastitis is one reason for loss of milk production within a herd, and it also accounts for a low snf figure. As a sub-clinical infection it can cause a reduction in snf of the order of 0·2 per cent. This is mainly due to a drop in lactose and casein in the milk.

TAINTS IN MILK

Taints in milk arise either from foods eaten by the cow, or from odours absorbed from the atmosphere by the milk.

Taints from foods are most likely if feeding occurs just before milking and it is now a common practice to limit foods such as kale, swedes and silage before milking.

Beet tops are particularly liable to taint milk if consumed in a semi-decayed state. They should be fed reasonably fresh, after a wilting period of at least 48 hours.

Certain weeds will cause taints in milk—the chief one being garlic, a common weed of hedge bottoms.

Odours from disinfectants or fly sprays can cause taints which are absorbed from the atmosphere; it should always be a general practice to keep the dairy as fresh as possible.

VICES IN DAIRY COWS

Kicking. The correct handling of the down-calving heifer will induce good milking habits. Initially, cows kick from pain or fear, and once the habit is formed it is very difficult to break.

The usual method of restraining a confirmed kicker is by passing a rope in figure-of-eight fashion around the hind legs above the hocks and pulling tight. This prevents either leg being used to kick at the milker. Another method is to pass a rope forward of the pelvic or hip bones round the abdomen and pull tight; this, in my

A cow down with milk fever being given a calcium borogluconate injection. Where there is a previous history of milk fever attacks it is a good idea to be prepared to give such an injection as a preventive before calving.

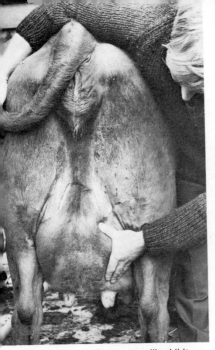

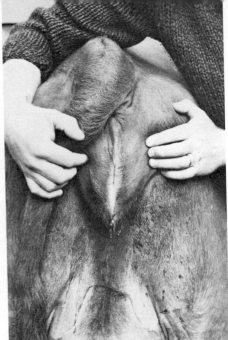

As calving time approaches a cow will exhibit easily recognisable symptoms. Several days beforehand the udder will start to fill out and project at the back, and will feel hard to the touch.

The tailhead muscles will slacken and, as the pelvics widen, a sunken area will appear between each pin bone and the root of the tail. At first these hollows will take a finger; just before calving they become big enough to take a fist.

The vagina will become grossly englarged. The lips will part slightly, the inner tissue becomes pinker and there will be a discharge of mucus.

Twelve hours before calving the udder will be fully distended and pressure with the fingers will leave quite deep and lasting impressions. The teats will be stiff, as an aid to suckling by the new-born calf.

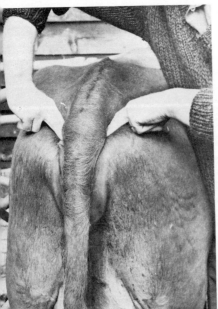

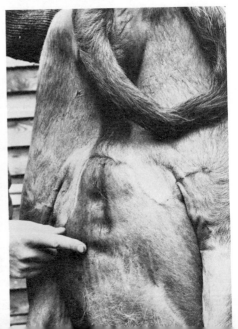

Above: When help at calving is necessary fix a calving rope around the fetlock of first foot to appear. Then attach rope to second foot when that appears. When traction is applied on the rope, direction of pull should be downwards (right).

Left: Close-up of a farm-built service crate inside a bull yard. The ramps are designed to take some of the weight off the cow when an old, heavy bull is being used.

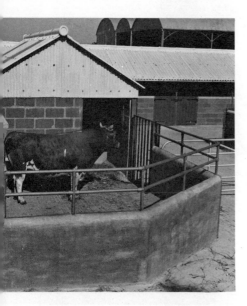

Centre and bottom: Modern bull accommodation allows the bull a good view of what is going on around him. This prevents loneliness and frustration and thus reduces the chance of his become infertile.

view is a less satisfactory method. Restraint in the form of a kicking bar can be used. This places a constraint upon the flank.

Always remember that the closer to the cow one stands while milking, the less harm she can do should she kick out.

The quiet but firm handling of cows is essential to good cow-manship. Where a cow kicks or is restless while being milked, consistent patience and gentleness are often more effective than forceful means of restraint.

Restraining methods should only be used after all other efforts have failed.

Suckling. Occasionally individual cows exhibit a tendency to suckle. This habit is established in calfhood and is discouraged if calves are housed singly when pail fed. There are available on the market various devices which are made in the form of a plate and these can be fastened through the nose of the offender.

SLOW MILKERS AND LEAKING TEATS

Hard or 'slow' milkers are usually so because of unusually small teat orifices. The condition may be overcome by veterinary treatment using teat expanders, or by a delicate surgical operation which severs some of the sphincter muscles.

Such practices are always attended by the risk of mastitis infection.

The problem of leaking teats due to wide teat orifices can be temporarily met by sealing the teats immediately after milking by dipping them into collodion or by passing a rubber band round them.

Neither is a permanent cure and the best plan is to milk these animals more frequently. If a rubber band is used, care must be taken that it applies only sufficient pressure to stop the milk flow; it must not cause pain.

Pea In Teat

Occasionally an internal growth or 'pea' develops in the teat canal which makes milking slow and difficult. The obstruction may be removed by a veterinary operation.

Sore Teats

In cases of sore teats the pain caused while milking can be ameliorated by rubbing in udder ointment which softens the skin of the teat and promotes healing.

Before the subject of cow management is closed, I feel it is necessary to stress again how important is the personal factor.

The good herdsman is on terms of quiet confidence and affection with his cows. He should be able to approach them readily, even in the field, and at the same time be recognised as their master. At no time should milking cows be roughly handled, hurriedly driven or shouted at.

A good herdsman is regular and meticulous in his routine, as cows are essentially creatures of habit, and show resentment or nervous excitement when their daily routine is upset. I believe the high-yielding cow must be a happy cow and that she can suffer unhappiness in very real fashion.

The faculty of really observing cows with a discerning and critical eye is not a gift possessed by all men, but to the first-class stockman it is essential. Early recognition of disease or symptoms of ill-health, even to the extent of just a loss of appetite, however slight, can mean so much if observed at once. A good stockman is a key worker on any dairy farm. Without such a man the best-planned schemes will never reach fulfilment.

How Recording Helps

One of the less appreciated advantages of joining the official milk recording shemes is that record-keeping becomes a regular routine. The recording of calving dates, service dates and notes as to when cows are sick is provided for on the milk weighing sheets, and the Milk Record Book provides a summary of each cow's history during the milk recording year.

This is all most valuable information. It is essential to the farmer in planning a breeding programme; it is essential to the stockman in day-to-day herd management, and it is especially useful to the veterinary surgeon when he is called in.

Where herds are not officially recorded some form of herd records should be maintained. The effort and time they involve will be more than fully repaid.

Many details will be found of significance as the records build up. For example, irregular heat periods, coming at less than 18 days or more than 24 days, must indicate things like hormone imbalance of either the male or female reproductive organs or some mechanical failure of either of these. For this reason, I would recommend that all heat periods should be recorded whether the animal is served or not.

A recent introduction on many farms has been the Breeding Board. There are many types but they all perform the same task.

The information provided by a breeding board will be:

● a record of all heats observed, giving the regular cycle of heat periods;
● the first service, and any recurrence of heat periods;
● second and further services;
● confirmation of pregnancy;
● the date of next calving;
● the dry period calculated with reference to next calving date.

With this information to hand the herdsman is keeping in touch with the breeding calendar of the herd on a day-to-day basis. Where cows are repeatedly failing to conceive to service, this is shown up clearly by the Breeding Board and veterinary help can be enlisted immediately. Ideally the veterinary surgeon should be used on a regular consultative basis; the herd health should be discussed regularly and in many cases problems identified before they become too serious.

Food Recording
One form of recording that is particularly valuable because of its relation to the cost of milk production is food recording. Indeed, I believe that it is as important to know how much food the herd consumes as it is to know how much the individual cows yield.

For example, supposing a herd of 120 cows: 90 cows in milk with milk production for the previous week being 8172 kg, and feeding at 0·4 kg/litre over 4·5 kg.

Milk from bulk = 4·5 kg × 90 cows × 7 days = 2835 kg milk.

● The yield from concentrates during the week was: 8172 minus 2835 kg = 5337 kg milk.
● The amount of concentrates required to produce 5337 kg milk at 0·4 kg /litre = 2134 kg concentrates.
● Add concentrates fed to dry cows = 381 kg.
● Total concentrate requirement in the week was 2515 kg.

The next step is to make sure that this is the amount of concentrate that should have been fed. If there is a discrepancy, this must be investigated.

PROBLEM OF BULK FEEDING

Hay is much easier to ration accurately if it is baled rather than loose. The skilled cowman must be able to judge accurately the amount of hay he feeds. Baled hay can vary widely in weight, but once the cowman has had sufficient practice in actually weighing hay, he should be able to judge the weight fed to within 10 per cent.

Silage is less easy to ration. For one thing its dry-matter content is much more variable. Nevertheless, a real attempt should be made to judge the weight fed, by weighing the occasional forkful and allowing for any variation in dry-matter percentage (see Chapter 7).

Roots like mangolds, swedes or beet tops are often fed at pasture when individual feeding of the cows is impossible. But the weight in a cart- or trailer-load should be estimated from cubic capacity.

Kale, or other crops rationed by electric fencing, should be check-weighed before folding begins in order to determine the crop yield. Due allowance should be made for waste.

It is only if the actual quantities fed are known that a check can be made on the quality of home-grown foods. If the rations fed prove in practice to be inadequate, as would be shown by a too rapid decline in milk yield, or by loss of condition, then the quality of the home-grown foods has been over-estimated.

The cow is the best judge of their feeding value, but unless actual consumption is known the farmer is in no position to judge their adequacy. Home-grown foods exhibit a much wider range in feeding value than purchased concentrates.

Therefore, feeding of bulk feeds, employing high proportions of home-grown foods, needs intelligent stockmanship if results are to be satisfactory. Rule-of-thumb methods will not do.

The old concept of $3\frac{1}{2}$lb of concentrates per gallon ($0 \cdot 33$ kg concentrates per 1 kg milk) has no equivalent when it comes to feeding silage and other bulk foods. The farmer has to make every effort to try and assess the value of his own material in terms of weight required for maintenance or per litre of milk.

Analyses can be of great help, but protein percentage alone is of little guide to the feeding value of the grassland products such as silage, hay or dried grass, unless the fibre percentage—indicative of the stage of growth of the conserved material—is also known.

In the future, laboratory assessment of the feeding value of feeds will include a measure of digestibility which, as already pointed out, falls markedly from around 70–80 per cent with young conserved herbage and concentrates to 50 per cent or below for mature fodder such as cereal straws.

CHAPTER 14

BREEDING BETTER DAIRY COWS

To be successful in the art of cattle breeding it is necessary to understand the principles of inheritance in cattle.

In each body cell there are numerous pairs of genes. Each pair controls some particular characteristic of the animal's make-up.

These can be 'identical'—as they would be if both the genes controlling hair colour were the same; or they can be 'mixed'—as they would be if one gene for hair colour was for red and the other for black.

When a mating takes place between a bull and a cow the bull contributes one gene for each characteristic he possesses and the cow also contributes one gene for each characteristic she possesses. These unite as pairs in the calf born as a result of that mating.

There is no way of controlling which gene the bull or cow passes on from each pair it possesses. That is a matter of chance.

Therefore, if a cow has mixed genes for hair colour—one for red and one for black—and the bull also has mixed genes for the same character, the calf from their mating will have one of three possible combinations of genes for hair colour:

> Two genes for black;
> Two genes for red;
> One gene for black and one for red.

If one of the animals has identical genes for hair colour—say, both for red—and the other has mixed genes—one for red and one for black—the calf born from them will have one of two possible combinations of genes for hair colour:

> Two genes for red;
> One gene for red and one for black.

Where the bull has identical genes for one colour—black, and

Principles of

How Good and
are passed from

Every cow and bull has in each body cell many pairs of genes. Each pair controls one particular character of the beast's make-up—horns, colour, etc.

One gene from each pair is carried by bull's sperm and cow's ovum at time of reproduction. These unite and thus the developing calf gets two genes for every character. Which gene each parent passes on is a matter of chance.

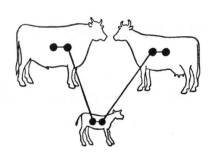

The two genes of a pair can be identical (thus, in the pair of genes controlling hair colour, they could both be for red) or a pair may be mixed (in which case one may be for red colour and one for white).

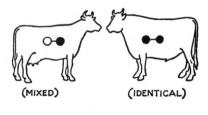

(MIXED)   (IDENTICAL)

Where both parents have identical genes for a certain character it does not matter which of the pairs passes from parents to calf. The result will be the same. Their calves will always have identical genes for this character.

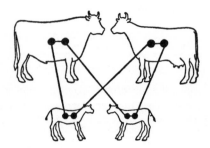

Inheritance

Bad Characteristics
Parents to Calves

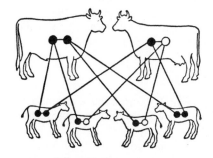

But if one parent has identical genes for a certain character and the other. has mixed genes, then half the calves born will have identical genes for this factor and the other half will have mixed genes.

Where both parents have mixed genes for a certain factor, then $\frac{1}{4}$ of the calves will have identical genes of one kind, $\frac{1}{4}$ will have identical genes of another kind and $\frac{1}{2}$ of the calves will have mixed genes.

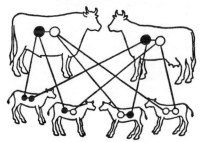

So far, the breeding examples quoted have been on simple body characters like hair colour controlled by one pair of genes. Milk production is determined not by one pair of genes but by many pairs each controlling various factors. These genes cannot be examined to determine whether they are identical or mixed.

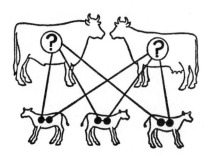

The only way of finding out whether animals breed true for milk is by knowing whether all their progeny consistently produce good yields. This is a sound indication that the parents have identical genes for many of the factors influencing milk production.

the cow has identical genes for the other colour—red, the calf will have only one possible combination of genes for that characteristic:

One for red and one for black.

But where the bull and the cow both have identical genes for the same colour—say red—the calf can only have:

Two genes for red.

Thus it will be clear that the only way of ensuring that a calf has certain desired characteristics is to breed from parents that have those desired characteristics in the form of identical genes. Such animals are known by the scientist as 'pure' or homozygous.

PROGENY GIVE THE CLUE

But the great problem is that animals cannot be examined to determine what genes they have; the only way of knowing is by the uniformity of their offspring.

For example, where a cow and bull consistently produce a red-coated calf from each mating it is reasonable to assume both are pure for this particular factor.

The issue is greatly complicated when it comes to breeding for milk production because this is determined not by one pair of genes but by many pairs each controlling certain associated factors. None of these factors can be seen by the eye.

Therefore, breeding for high yields is essentially a matter of finding out which animals will consistently produce high-yielding progeny, and then to regard these animals as foundation stock in herd building.

This is the most certain method of breed improvement.

To select breeding stock on their own performance or appearance is a gamble. The fact that they conform to certain body characteristics or produce so much milk is no guarantee they will pass these attributes on.

And to select on the basis of ancestry—the pedigree system— is also a gamble. For although milk records for a cow's dam and granddam may give some guide to the cow's milking qualities, the only true index of the merit of a bull for breeding purposes is his progeny records. By obtaining the milk records of a bull's daughters, his transmitting ability for milk production can be most accurately assessed.

TESTING A BULL

A true bull progeny test should preferably include all the bull's daughters. Failing that it should cover a minimum sample of ten (e.g. one year's crop). Further, the conditions of feeding and management under which the daughters are milked should be known, so that a comparison can be made with their dam's yields.

The most important factors here are the age at first calving and frequency of milking—i.e. whether milking twice daily or thrice daily. In other words, the milk records must be a fair indication of what the daughters can be expected to do under the conditions the purchaser will be able to maintain in his own herd.

TESTING A COW
With a cow, a progeny test of her daughters gives guiding information as to the transmitting ability of the dam, which may be very different from her own milk record.

Cows of unknown breeding may be high producers themselves, but because of their mixed genetic make up—i.e. heterozygosity rather than homozygosity—they may never breed a daughter of similar productivity.

The tendency is for such cows to produce progeny of breed average production—what the geneticist terms 'regression to breed average'. But cows that, by virtue of long and productive lives, leave two or more high-producing daughters, are regarded as proven dams and should, other things being equal, become the dams of future stock bulls.

PRESENTATION OF PROGENY TEST RESULTS

1. Breeding Index Based on Dam-Daughter Comparisons
The earliest work on progeny testing attempted to rate a bull on the performance of at least ten of his daughters compared to their dams. Thus if the progeny averaged 4086 kg in their heifer lactation compared to 3995 kg in the same first lactations of their dams, the bull was given a milk transmission index X given by the formula

$$\left(\frac{3995 + X}{2} = 4086 \therefore X = 4177 \right)$$

This formula assumes that the milk yield of the dam is an indication of her milk transmitting ability, which is a fallacy. It can be further criticised in that where dams and daughters have not been reared and milked under exactly similar environmental conditions, environmental differences may completely mask any genetic difference between the two generations.

For example, if the dams were milked under conditions of food shortage, a bull could later have been credited with a high index merely because his daughters gave higher yields when more adequately fed.

The use of such an index is also limited to large herds with at least ten daughters available for testing, and herds of some standing as self-contained breeding units. In other words, environmental effects were so strong as to invalidate this mathematical attempt to reduce a bull's breeding value to a definite milk 'index'.

2. Breeding Index Based on Contemporary Comparisons—CC

This method was previously used by the MMB with its AI stud to overcome the problems of environment by comparing the milk yields of the progeny of bulls with each other, the bulls being contemporaries in the AI stud.

The extent to which a bull raises or lowers the milk yields of his progeny, compared to the progeny of other bulls used in the same herds at the same time, gives a 'contemporary comparison' rating to that bull of $\pm X$ gallons. Many bulls, perhaps four out of five, breed average or near-average progeny, while the odd outstanding bull will have a plus rating of 360 kg or more, or a ten per cent increase on his contemporaries.

It will be realised that this system of testing, so applicable to AI, where a selected group of young bulls can be progeny-tested over many herds (which must be milk recorded under NMR), is not applicable to individual herds because of lack of progeny numbers. Pedigree breeders, however, are now co-operating to make this possible by group breeding projects.

3. Breeding Index Based on Improved Contemporary Comparisons—ICC

A bull tested in many herds against other bulls of average merit may have a high contemporary comparison. This would be likely to enable him to be selected for use in herds where superior bulls were used as a regular breeding policy. His daughters in these herds would then be compared to daughters of high CC bulls, so his own contemporary comparison appears to decline.

Generally, testing of young bulls is more difficult because of the fact that, after selection on pedigree herds, they are tested in herds against established bulls.

Improved contemporary comparison will make allowances for the merit of contemporary heifers. If they are by bulls with a plus bonus, their lactation records will be adjusted downwards by the amount of their sires' ICC and vice versa. These adjustments will give a much truer indication of the actual breeding merit of an individual bull and will eliminate the drops in production bonuses usually experienced when the second-crop daughters complete their first lactations.

Other corrections made to the milk records are concerned with age at calving and the month of calving. Only records of heifers between the ages of 22 and 38 months are included in the calculations; corrections are added or subtracted according to calving age. Older heifers tend to give more milk anyway, a feature unconnected with season of calving or genetic ability.

Month of calving has an effect upon lactation yield. Autumn-calvers tend to yield more than spring calvers; therefore a correction for this feature is also applied in determining the ICC. The system is in operation throughout England, Wales and Scotland.

The main advantage of the ICC system is that the indication of performance is independent of individual management factors. Bulls with good production bonuses (ICC Rating) are likely to produce production-improved results in a herd irrespective of the management of the herd.

FIVE AIMS IN BREEDING

Against this background a dairy farmer can set out the full objectives at which he needs to aim if he is going to build up a herd in which every female approaches as nearly as possible the 'ideal cow'.

I suggest that his objectives should be:

1. To breed cows capable of making most efficient use of foods, i.e. of high feed-conversion efficiency.

2. To breed cows capable of high production, for that is fundamental to increased efficiency in milk production; it lowers cost per litre in respect of feeding and overhead expenses.

3. To breed cows which will give milk of the required compositional quality to meet consumer demand.

4. To breed cows that possess the qualities of longevity and disease-resistance—both closely related factors. A long life per cow means fewer replacements. Further, in many cases today, rearing costs are not paid off until a cow has completed two lactations.

5. To breed cows of good milking temperament—docile to handle and quick to let down their milk.

Finally, where a dairy farmer is also a pedigree breeder, he must have as his objective the breed society standards of type, colour, markings etc. Many of these characteristics are trade marks of the breed and not essential economic factors.

DAIRY PROGENY TESTING SCHEME

With the widespread use of AI the breeding of bulls has largely gone out of the hands of the average dairy farmer. The Marketing Board in England and Wales has a scheme for the progeny-testing of young Friesian bulls with which dairy farmers are asked to co-operate. This scheme is briefly described.

1. The farmer offers a minimum of twelve cows in the herd to be bred to young bulls.

2. Cash payments are made for each identified calf sired by a DPTS sire, also for every heifer which completes its first lactation in the herd.

3. Somewhere in the region of 130–150 bulls a year are tested in the scheme and up to 2500 farmers participate in the scheme.

4. After use, bulls are laid off until progeny test results are available. One bull in seven on average returns to the AI stud.

CONTRACT MATING

In addition to the selection of bulls there is a scheme for the contract mating of cows. Information from Milk Records is scrutinised for cows with very good records, emphasis being placed on selection for weight of butterfat. Cows for contract mating are selected for breeding potential rather than on absolute production records. The selection process is based on the cow's Estimated Transmitting Ability (ETA) which is an estimate of her genetic worth, taking into account her own production records and her sire's ICC figure. By taking into account the proposed contract mating sire's ICC data, it is possible to obtain an ETA of a son from a planned mating.

BREEDING SYSTEMS

At this point the various systems of breeding can be discussed; each is briefly outlined in the following sections.

Inbreeding
This is where mating occurs within the family but only between successive generations, e.g. father to daughter or mother to son.

This particularly close breeding leads to an intensification of characteristics—both good and bad. If the parent stock is uniformly good, free from undesirable factors in a hidden or recessive form, inbreeding will result in the perpetuation of the desirable characteristics without their being weakened from outside sources, and a highly uniform family can be built up this way.

Unfortunately, most of our dairy cattle are not free from undesirable factors—low milk or fat yield, low fertility, or lethal characters like 'bull dog' calves—and these are not revealed until close inbreeding is adopted.

Inbred Families

With inbreeding, therefore, one plays for high stakes but the risk of failure is increased. Nevertheless, in the long run a highly inbred successful family would represent the cream or elite of breeding material. It would be the nearest approach to the pure or homozygous state, which alone can fulfil the dictum that 'like begets like'.

Because of the great financial risks involved in pursuing inbreeding as a herd policy, most breeders nowadays choose to mate their cattle less closely.

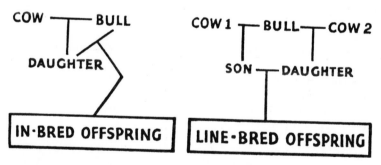

Line Breeding

This involves mating to a succession of related sires. It tends to reduce the degree of variability in the herd, without incurring the risks involved in inbreeding. Line breeding in its commonest form takes the course of son following father as herd sire; under this system a bull could be mated with his half-sisters.

Outcrossing

This is the policy of mating without particular reference to families; a bull being used may have no blood relation to any of the females in the herd.

The results from an outcross have no permanence beyond the first generation. But it may be necessary to resort to outcrossing where a breeder desires to improve his herd in any particular character (e.g. butterfat percentage), and feels that he has no suitable material in his own herd from which to breed for this improvement.

Hybrids, e.g. Jersey × Friesian, show promise in higher fertility and greater viability of the calves (hybrid vigour).

CHARACTERISTICS FOR WHICH TO BREED

It should be realised, however, that no breeding system is infallible. Results depend entirely on the genetic make-up of the parental material. Results often attributed to a particular system of mating are due in most cases more to the use of a particularly outstanding bull.

The most certain means of improving a herd is by the use of a succession of proven sires—proven if possible within the herd.

I have previously given a brief outline of the objectives a dairy farmer should have in his breeding programme. It may help at this stage to show what is known about the inheritance of some of the characteristics for which he will be trying to breed.

Size

There is evidence that, within a breed, size is correlated with production. Although large animals may not be any more efficient than small ones, they save in labour and housing, and thus reduce those costs per litre of milk produced.

Consequently, size is a desirable objective. It is definitely inherited and can be bred for.

Digestive Capacity

Cows vary widely in their ability to digest roughage foods. At the Minnesota Station the ability to consume hay was found to vary from 1·25 to 2 kg per 50 kg liveweight per cow per day.

My observations lead me to regard the ability of a cow to maintain a high yield at pasture, without heavy supplementary feeding, as an indication that she has a high digestive capacity for bulky foods. It is worth noting the varying abilities of cows in this respect.

Udder Shape, Size and Texture

These are all inherited characters and must be bred for, though their inheritance is a complex problem.

Milk and Fat Production

They appear to be separately inherited. And it seems that, within each breed, there is a fairly constant inheritance of butterfat in terms of kilograms per lactation. The butterfat percentage is not inherited as such, being raised or lowered according to yield of milk achieved.

To illustrate this point, Table 14.1 shows details in respect of one cow with two daughters by different bulls.

Table 14.1.

Dam
Records of:
5366 kg at 3·37 per cent ..... 3rd lactation
5312 kg at 3·72 per cent ..... 4th lactation

Daughter by Bull A
Records of:
5366 kg at 3·30 per cent ..... 1st lactation
5285 kg at 3·27 per cent .....2nd lactation

Daughter by Bull B
Records of:
4190 kg at 4·03 per cent ..... 1st lactation
6111 kg at 3·86 per cent .....2nd lactation

The comparison of daughters on the basis of yield, butterfat percentage and pounds of butterfat is as shown in Table 14.2.

Table 14.2

Lactation	Milk Yield kg	Butterfat per cent	kg
1st			
Daughter 1	5366	3·30	177
Daughter 2	4190	4·03	169
2nd			
Daughter 1	5285	3·27	172
Daughter 2	6111	3·86	236

This shows how butterfat production varies less than the butterfat percentage, but with payment for milk related to total solids basis (rather than solely on butterfat production) present breeding policies must be aimed at raising the total solids in milk. Attention must thus be given to snf percentage which is closely related to butterfat percentage in inheritance.

Persistency of Lactation
Though persistency of lactation is profoundly affected by the level of feeding and general management, it is also an inherited characteristic and a desirable quality in breeding stock.

Milking Aptitude
Slow or hard milkers are likely to pass on these characteristics to their progeny. Cows which, for temperamental reasons, fail to let down their milk properly, often show wide daily variations in yield and low persistency of lactation.

To complete this chapter, reference must be made to the various breed societies and their work to promote better breeding.

BREED SOCIETIES

In the early history of breed societies, inspection characters such as colour markings which readily 'trade mark' the breed were given considerable prominence. They still are, but most societies today are paying more and more attention to improving the economic characters of registered pedigree cattle.

These efforts at breed improvement take the following forms:

1. The formation of an elite register of outstanding cows and bulls, based on the milk production records of the former—either by lactations or by lifetime performance—and on daughter's milk records (i.e. progeny records) for the latter.

Entry to such a register confers a distinction to the animal concerned and indicates real merit.

But the basis of entry for bulls on a minimum number of qualifying daughters—usually ten—is unfair to bulls being used in small herds with limited progeny numbers. A better method would be to insist on a minimum proportion of qualifying daughters out of each bull's total registered progeny.

2. To make known the breeding performance of bulls registered as soon as sufficient evidence of their progeny's milking capacity is known. This avoids the premature slaughter of good bulls.

3. To promote by competitions and specially sponsored sales a real interest and demand for pedigree cattle of proven performance.

4. Lastly, most societies run schemes for grading up non-pedigree cattle to pedigree status. This may be over a period of three to five generations, based on qualifying standards of inspection and milk yields for the foundation stock, followed by the use of a succession of purebred sires.

By this means, a dairy farmer of limited capital resources is able over the years eventually to own a full pedigree herd; and the breed itself often benefits by the introduction of fresh blood.

Cow classification according to type has been adopted by all the leading societies; this means that pedigree cattle are classified by a panel of judges according to type as laid down by the respective breed society. This information is incorporated in subsequent pedigrees—the common classifications are excellent, very good and good.

WHERE PROGRESS LIES

From what has been written, it will be realised that the breeding of dairy cattle has become a highly technical business, particularly in regard to the breeding of bulls, on which the future of any breed ultimately depends.

Today it will be found that within most breeds there is a hard-core of master breeders, with high-producing herds, who supply the 'best' of the bulls in the breed. These bulls are mostly bought by the second strata of breeders who also keep pedigree herds but pursue less ambitious breeding policies and probably attain a lower standard of general management.

These latter herds do, however, supply pedigree bulls for use in the commercial herds of the ordinary milk-producing farmer. They act, as it were, more as multipliers of useful bulls rather than as specialised constructive breeders.

Real progress within the breed rests, therefore, on the elite breeders.

In their herds a consistent breeding policy over many years is essential. Most herds which make their mark in breed improvement are of long standing. Ten years—which is more than the span of life of the average pedigree herd—is only three generations of breeding. And that is far too short a time to make any real contribution to breed improvement.

The dispersal of highly productive and old-established herds is always a tragedy as far as constructive breeding is concerned, but affords the best opportunity for others to secure good blood for their own herd-improvement programmes.

CHAPTER 15

BULL MANAGEMENT

ALL the advantages of progeny testing will be lost if by the time the test is completed—say by five and half years of age at the earliest—the bull concerned is dead. Yet this is often the case.

On many farms the early disposal of a bull is due primarily to the lack of suitable housing. As bulls get older their tempers usually deteriorate and they become more difficult to handle unless controlled by specially designed buildings and apparatus.

GOOD HOUSING

Proper housing for stock bulls is therefore essential to any long-term breeding programme. So is a policy of good bull management. The temperament of a bull is firstly conditioned by heredity, but even a quiet animal can be ruined by wrong methods of handling.

The essentials of good bull accommodation are:

1. A strongly-built loose-box, minimum dimensions 3 m × 3 m with smooth inside walls, opening on to an exercise yard of double that area. The feeding manger in the box should be placed so that the bull can be fed from outside the box.

2. Overhead, from inside the box, above the feeding manger and along the full length of the yard should run a stout steel cable to which the bull is attached by a chain (with two or three swivel links) which passes through his ring and around his horns.

In polled breeds a head collar can be fitted to which the chain can be attached at the top of the bull's head, mid-way between the ears.

The length of the tethering chain is important. It should equal the height of the overhead wire above ground level; then it will not prevent the bull from lying down or foul his forelegs when he does lie down.

Secured in this manner the bull is perfectly free to take exercise but is sufficiently under control and can be caught and secured without the stockman entering the yard or box.

3. Built in to the yard should be a service crate to which a cow can be admitted for service. A gate normally shutting off the crate from the exercise yard is then opened to admit the bull without releasing him from his overhead tether.

I have found that this method ensures complete safety to the stockman, even with vicious bulls.

SITING THE BULL PEN

With old and heavy bulls, it is often considered necessary to use a service ramp to take the weight off the cow. In theory the idea is sound; in practice I have found some bulls refuse to serve from a ramp, particularly if they have never done so when young.

The situation of the bull pen should be carefully considered.

Bulls can become frustrated and lonely. In such circumstances the habit of masturbation may develop and may lead to infertility. When bulls can take an interest in their surroundings the chances of infertility may be reduced. For this reason it is an advantage to have tubular metal rails for the bull yard and to site the building so the bull can see what goes on.

The bull box itself should be built solidly and provide a sheltered retreat from the rigours of winter and the hot sun of summer.

As a calf, a bull should be taught to lead and to recognise man as his master and friend. At ten months of age he should be rung.

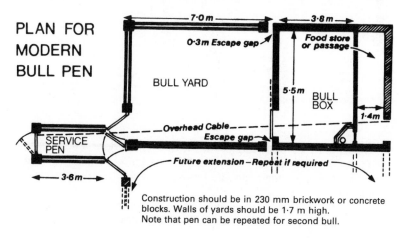

PLAN FOR MODERN BULL PEN

7·0 m

3·8 m

0·3m Escape gap

Food store or passage

BULL YARD

5·5 m

BULL BOX

1·4m

Overhead Cable

Escape gap

SERVICE PEN

Future extension—Repeat if required

3·6 m

Construction should be in 230 mm brickwork or concrete blocks. Walls of yards should be 1·7 m high.
Note that pen can be repeated for second bull.

ALTERNATIVE METHOD
OF BULL HOUSING

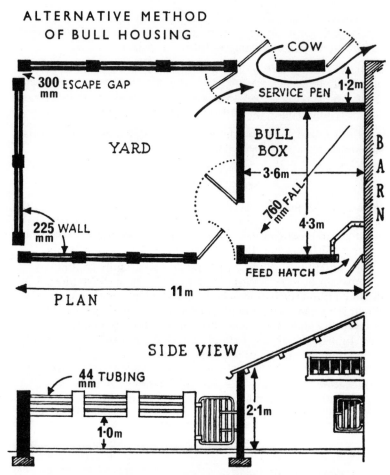

This bull pen layout allows most routine jobs such as feeding and mating to be seen to without going into the pen. Main structure is 230 mm brickwork or concrete blocks and roof of asbestos cement. Safety measures must be built in for the operator. If in doubt approach the Health and Safety Executive.

This is done by punching in the septum of the nose a hole large enough to allow a coppper ring of 51–63 mm diameter to be inserted. Self-piercing rings can be used if a suitable punch is not available.

When being led as a youngster, a short piece of rope through the ring enables the bull's head to held up; with older bulls a bull

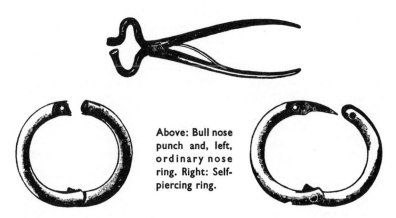

Above: Bull nose punch and, left, ordinary nose ring. Right: Self-piercing ring.

staff is used for the same purpose. A bull charges with his head down, and he can do little harm to the stockman provided is head is held high.

HANDLING IS ESSENTIAL

Regular handling of bulls is essential; if this is not done as a routine they may become resentful and truculent. I remember one breeder who refused to have automatic water bowls fitted to his bull pens simply to ensure that the bulls had to be led to water daily and thus had regular exercise and regular handling.

It is most unwise to take liberties with older bulls as they often suffer sudden deterioration of temper, and once a bull knows his strength and appreciates that the stockmen are afraid of him, he is potentially dangerous. Such a bull should be masked to ensure safety of the men who handle him.

In addition to proper handling a bull requires certain regular attention to health details and, of course, proper feeding. These matters are discussed below.

Unless a bull is adequately exercised on a hard surface, his feet will grow out of shape. This tends to make service painful, particularly if the hind feet are affected. Hooves should not be allowed to grow long and proper trimming of the feet should, where necessary, be a regular routine.

PREVENTING FOOTROT

When a bull is regularly exercised it will pay to walk him through the cows' footbath (see chapter 17) as a preventative against footrot. Where regular exercise is not possible, it is a good plan to have a footbath built beneath the foot-trimming stocks.

Incidentally, a bull should be introduced gradually to these devices in the same way that a heifer is introduced to the milking shed. Begin by fastening the bull up in the pen a few times so that he becomes used to it before the regular operation of foot-trimming starts.

In the winter, a bull often becomes infected with lice. I recommend that every autumn, the neck, withers and spine of the bull should be clipped to reduce of risk of attack, and that monthly dusting with insecticide should continue all winter, paying particular attention to the top of the head, behind the ears and the root of the tail.

In summer a proprietary fly spray will help to reduce worry from flies and possible bad temper, particularly where bulls are tethered in the open without shade.

Tethering is commendable as it affords the bull both freedom and change of diet. It is simple enough in practice, whether you use a specially designed tether or merely a steel rope anchored to a heavy concrete block. The chief mistake to avoid is to use too long a tethering chain which will foul the bull's forelegs.

The usual practice, during the grazing season, is to tether a bull four to six hours in the daytime and return him to his box at night. This eliminates the need for providing water while the bull is tethered.

In hot weather it is a good practice to tether by night and return the bull to his box during the day. This prevents heat exhaustion and considerably reduces fly worrying.

AGE FOR SERVICE

A young bull may be used sparingly from ten months until he is sexually mature—at about two years of age. In the first year, most young bulls can be safely mated with, say, twenty bulling heifers such as was earlier suggested as a test mating for progeny testing.

Over-use of a young bull may lead to temporary impotence or even complete sterility. Four matings per week would be the limit.

If sufficiently well fed, older bulls can be worked harder and in many herds which aim at autumn calvings, the period of greatest activity for the bulls is in mid-winter. After a long period of inactivity a bull may be temporary infertile for a few services only owing to low-virility semen; thus, after such a rest period, I usually allow two services per cow rather than the normal one for the first few days.

Time of Service

A cow is most likely to conceive to service towards the end of the heat period: this is explained by the fact that the egg is released from the ovary and has had time to move down the fallopian tubes to meet the sperm.

FEEDING GUIDE

Bulls are at least 100 kg heavier than the breed average for cows, and a typical dairy ration for a bull in mature breeding condition would be:

0·68 kg good hay ⎱
0·68 kg silage or kale ⎰ per 50 kg liveweight
plus 1·8–2·7 kg concentrates.

Thus a bull of 600 kg liveweight would receive:

8 kg good hay,
8 kg silage, kale or cabbages etc.,
and 1·8–2·7 kg concentrates.

The concentrates can be the production concentrate fed to the herd or a mixture, with a level of 16–18 per cent DCP, made up as follows:

Oats and/or beet pulp	2 parts
Barley and/or flaked maize	1 part
High-protein cake	1½ parts
or White fishmeal	1 part.

A bull should not be fed immediately before use, as he works better on an empty stomach. Neither should he be fed heavily on low-quality hay or straw, otherwise he will tend to become too paunchy and slow in service.

During the grazing season when a bull is tethered on good-quality grass, he should still receive a little hay—up to, say, 3·2 kg daily—and about 1·4 kg concentrates.

The concentrates should be cut out of the bull's ration entirely when he is not in active use. This aids economy in upkeep and also helps to preserve the bull's good temper.

A valuable bull deserves good treatment and must get it if his term of useful life is to be long. Much of the infertility in bulls is due to faulty nutrition.

Bull Licensing

The system of licensing bulls was abolished as from October 1976.

ARTIFICIAL INSEMINATION

Under the Agricultural (Artificial Insemination) Act of 1946, the Milk Marketing Board in England and Wales and the Scottish Boards have undertaken to provide AI facilities for farmers.

The Milk Marketing Boards operate from twenty-three main centres in England and Wales and three in Scotland (in Northern Ireland the AI Centres are run by the Ministry of Agriculture.) In addition, the Ministry of Agriculture has an AI Station at Shinfield, Reading, and there are five privately-operated AI Stations run by private enterprise.

Each centre has an advisory committee representing the NFU and the veterinary profession who, in conjunction with the field officers of the MMB in the case of Board centres, are responsible for inspection of progeny or near relatives of bulls offered to the AI service.

Notification for a service is, where possible, given to the centre concerned before 10 am when insemination is usually carried out that day. If notified after 10 am insemination is usually done early the next morning.

Advantages of AI

Since 1945 the development of AI has been extremely rapid in the United Kingdom. The major breed demand at the AI centres run by the Boards in England and Wales is given in Table 1.7.

The table shows the pattern of breed demand in AI. Over the past twenty years, the most significant feature has been the growth in demand for Friesian at the expense of the other dairy breeds.

The advantages of artificial insemination are greatest in small herds where the services of an expensive bull cannot be fully utilised. Equally, on small heavily-stocked farms the use of AI frees accommodation and food which can be used to keep another cow, thus raising income without additional capital expenditure.

The Board has for many years provided a service for the collection and freezing of semen from privately owned bulls either on one of its centres or on the owner's farm.

New regulations became operative in September 1977 and the AI Service offers a range of Farm Flask Services to farmers already using or planning to use Do-It-Yourself (DIY) inseminations. These services include the sale of flasks, semen, equipment, and DIY Training Courses.

The cost of the dairy bull of the day insemination under the

MMB Scheme is (1981) £4·60 for a first service, and £3·50 for the subsequent services. Extra charges are made where nominated bulls are requested and used.

Test Mating

Ideally the AI service should be from sires that have given a progeny test of outstanding merit. Such proven sires are hard to find, and still harder to purchase from privately owned herds. However, the Board is prepared to buy or hire such bulls provided that, in addition to being fully progeny tested, they also pass a veterinary examination for health and fertility, including the TB and Agglutination (Abortion) Tests and semen examination.

The advisory committee attached to each centre and the Livestock Husbandry Advisers of the Ministry of Agriculture also inspect the bull and his progeny or near female relatives.

Because of the shortage of proven sires, young bulls have to be employed by the AI service in order to meet the rapidly expanding demand. Details of the Progeny Testing Scheme are described in Chapter 14.

Breeding alone will not raise yields in a low-producing herd if management is at fault. In any case, it is a matter of some years before better bred cattle can find their place in the herd. Better breeding must go hand in hand with better standards of nutrition, hygiene and general management.

The AI centres offer a deep-freeze semen service to private breeders who can make a bank of frozen semem from their own private bulls. This service is of great value as an insurance against accidents or death with a particularly valuable bull.

Future Developments

Every encouragement must be given to the maintenance of the AI stud at the very highest level of performance, which depends on the quality of the bulls being reared mainly by private breeders. The Board is rearing bulls at Chippenham from selected matings of superior AI bulls on proven dams in pedigree milk-recorded herds, but the majority of bulls are still privately reared.

To encourage the private breeder, a system of royalties payable to the breeder has been suggested after a bull has been proven in the AI service. The Scottish MMB has introduced 'payments-on-results' scheme which may well herald a new approach to this problem.

Recent developments have been the formation by groups of prominent British Friesian breeders of cattle breeding groups to privately test bulls of their own breeding with the co-operation of the MMB. This is a further means of ensuring that the livelihood of the bull breeder is not jeopardised by the increasing use of AI.

Milk recording must be encouraged if the testing of young bulls is to be expeditiously carried out.

In recent years there has been an increased awareness of the opportunities which exist for cattle improvement on a world basis. British Semen Exports Ltd, founded in 1960, has since exported thousands of doses of semen to a total of fifty-five countries overseas. On the other hand, importations of cattle from overseas include Charolais, Canadian Holstein, Guernsey and Jersey bulls. In addition, a number of other European beef breeds, such as the Simmental and Limousin, have been introduced over the past few years.

All of these importations are prompted by the aim to improve the cattle in this and other countries by making use of AI and progeny-testing techniques which could again confer on these Islands the proud title of the 'Stud Farm of the World.'

CHAPTER 16

CALF REARING

THE necessity of rearing replacements for the milking herd imposes an additional burden on the resources of all dairy farms except those carrying flying herds.

On the basis of an average milking life of four years per cow it is necessary to rear every year at least one heifer per four cows in the herd, and that represents an appreciable cost.

There are two ways to keep this cost as low as possible. One is to increase the milking life of cows by better disease control so that fewer replacements are necessary; the other is economy in calf rearing.

Low costs in calf rearing are, in the main, achieved by restricting the quantity of whole milk consumed and using cheaper milk substitutes and calf-rearing foods. But it is false economy to carry

**Table 16.1. Target Live Weights over the Life of a
Friesian Heifer**

Age	*Weight* *kg*	*Liveweight gain* *kg per day*
Average birth weight	40	
5 weeks	55	0·5
3 months	85	0·5
6 months	140	0·6
12 months	270	0·7
Service	330	0·7
18 months	370	0·5
Just before calving	510	0·7
Just after calving	450	

(*Rearing Friesian Dairy Heifers*, MAFF.)

this too far. Permanently stunted growth due to faulty nutrition will result in a lowered production potential and a loss of revenue when the animal is in milk that will far outweigh the saving made at rearing time.

Dairy heifers must be reared on the modern dairy farm with a view to the amount of time which is to be allowed from birth to calving down as a heifer. It is very much a matter of opinion as to what a farmer may wish to do but the facts are simply that in the case of Freisian calves, at a birthweight of 40 kg, the requirement is to increase weight so that they weigh 510 kg immediately prior to calving. This gives a target of about 0·63 kg per day liveweight increase for a two-year calving heifer. If calving is extended to a 2½-year period, then the growth rate is less. This liveweight gain is not necessarily attained at the same rate all through the growing period. In early life, the first three months, the requirement is 0·5 kg/day increase; in the period 12–18 months the rate is 0·7 kg/day. The simple fact is that heifers must be big enough to serve (330 kg) at the right age, nine months before calving.

High liveweight gain during the winter period can be uneconomic, bearing in mind that there is compensation growth on grass during the early summer. The problem is usually that many heifers are left out on an off-lying field and cared for less than they should be. When summer grass deteriorates the heifers will not continue to grow unless they receive supplementary feed. On lowland farms the need is to conserve land for the milking cows, so it is desirable to have a two-year calving pattern. On farms with areas of marginal land such as banks and slopes, heifer rearing is not using potential cow pasture so calving is more likely to be at two and a half years.

The other factor to be considered is when the heifers are required to enter the herd as down calvers. Some herds are block calving, so heifers have to conform to a strict calving pattern of two years. Other herds have spread calving patterns; there is no pressure to calve early, except that land should be economically used and any extension beyond two and a half years' calving is likely to be uneconomic.

With a target calving date and weight in mind, it is then very important to give the calf a good start in life; the cow's first milk is essential.

Value of Colostrum

Unless calves are reared so that they achieve full growth with freedom from disease, the best-planned breeding programme will fail. So the aim should be to rear them at the lowest possible feeding costs consistent with normal frame and bodily development.

The colostrum secreted by the cow during the first four days in milk is of special significance in calf nutrition. Recent research has shown that it is absolutely vital that the calf should receive colostrum in the first six- to twelve-hour period.

Colostrum has the following properties:

- It contains most valuable antibodies which aid the calf to build up a resistance to bacterial diseases, such as white scour. The antibodies can only be passed through the abomasal wall undigested in the first 24 hours and possibly as early as the first 6 hours.
- It is highly digestible, having a nutritive value of some 40 per cent above ordinary milk giving a soft curd during the process of digestion.
- It is laxative in effect, and so helps in the expulsion of the foetal dung. The passage of this black jelly-like faecal matter usually indicates that the calf has suckled for the first time.
- Provided the dam has received adequate green food in the form of silage, kale, or dried grass, the colostrum is rich in carotene (the precursor of the health vitamin, Vitamin A, important for disease resistance.)

SUBSTITUTES FOR COLOSTRUM

Whenever possible newly-born calves should have colostrum; there is no adequate substitute for it.

Calves taken away from their dams at birth should be bucket-fed on their dams' milk for at least three or four days. And if a cow dies at calving or if she has been milked for longer than four days before calving, an effort should be made to obtain colostrum for her calf within six hours of birth. This can often be done by keeping the cow's colostrum in a refrigerator until the calf is born or by using surplus colostrum from another freshly-calved cow or by using colostrum from a cow that is being milked before calving and is still giving colostrum.

Where colostrum is not available from any source, then, as a last resort, a substitute can be used. A well-known recipe is:

Whip up a fresh egg in 0·85 litres of milk; add 0·28 litres of warm water, 1 teaspoonsful cod liver oil and 1 dessertspoonful castor oil. The quantities given will make one feed; give three feeds per day for at least four days. Once the calf has defecated normally, omit the castor oil from the mixture.

Before considering the various methods of calf rearing it is well to refer to work by Blaxter which has shown that a young calf has a high efficiency in using milk for growth. Further, when young it will make more rapid growth in proportion to the amount of food fed than it will at a later stage in life.

Therefore, restriction of milk or milk substitute at an early age can lead to stunted growth which can only be corrected later on by heavier and more expensive feeding.

This again points to the need for care in calf feeding so that economy is not carried too far.

Against this background the common methods of calf rearing can be outlined and discussed.

NURSE COW REARING

In this system the calves are left with their dams for the colostral period of four days and are then transferred to a nurse cow capable of suckling up to four calves at a time according to her milk yield.

Excellent calves can be reared by this method. It saves labour and, compared with pail feeding, it reduces calf mortality. It is the customary method of rearing bull calves for service.

Its main disadvantage is that it tends to be expensive if the value of milk is taken into account. Secondly, nurse cow rearing may predispose the calf to cross-suckling later in life, which is very undesirable. But, where suitable nurse cows are available—cows that are culled from the milking herd for reasons other than disease—it has much to recommend it.

Suckled calves usually develop more quickly than those reared by any other method.

The number of calves a nurse cow will rear must be adjusted to the yield of the cow so that each calf gets about 450 litres of milk over a period of twelve to sixteen weeks. Suckling three times a day is recommended for the first week; thereafter twice a day is satisfactory.

Calves can be weaned as soon as they are consuming adequate amounts of other foods, say, 2·3 kg of hay and 1·4 kg of concentrates a day. Then fresh young calves can be put to the cow, the number adjusted according to her declining yield.

It is, of course, essential to feed nurse cows on the same lines as those in the dairy herd so that their maintenance and production needs are fully met.

THE EARLY WEANING SYSTEM

The traditional method of feeding the calf with whole milk has been increasingly replaced by the 'early weaning' system. This change took place largely because the cost of milk substitute is almost half the price of whole milk and as such is a much more economic way of rearing calves.

In the early weaning system ideally no milk is fed after the colostral period of four days. Over the next five weeks, milk equivalent feeds are provided followed by weaning on to a ration wholly made up of dry feeds plus water. The system is described in detail in Table 16.2.

This system, by reducing the period of bucket feeding to five weeks, saves labour. And it saves accommodation by reducing the need for individual penning of the calves to five rather than twelve weeks—once weaned, calves can be penned communally according to age. By early consumption of dry foods, rearing costs are also reduced and early development of the rumen is encouraged.

It should be clearly understood that success in early weaning does depend on using good hay/straw to encourage rumination, and using concentrates of the highest feeding value to ensure an adequate nutrient intake by the calves.

THE AD-LIB FEEDING SYSTEM

The cold ad-lib acidified feeding system is rapidly gaining popularity. The milk powder is acidified so that the made-up liquid food will be preserved for a period of three days or more without going sour. This of course can be affected by weather conditions.

The acidified powder is mixed with water at the rate of 1·4 kg per ten litres. In cold weather it is advisable to take the chill off the water before mixing.

The acidified milk substitute is fed from teats which run on a pipeline from drums of 150–200 litres capacity. It is usual to allow one teat per six calves. The drums should be provided with lids.

One of the attractions of the system is the grouping of calves and avoidance of cleaning individual pens and feeding equipment.

Group pens should have rendered walls where calves are in contact with them and, since more liquid is consumed and voided by calves, a concrete floor with a good fall and drainage. The average daily intake would be eight litres of acidified milk substitute.

Table 16.2. The Early Weaning System

1. Feeding during the first five weeks of life
1–4 days colostrum fed as above.
A standard mix for milk equivalent is 125 g/litre for 2 × feeding.

5–10 days

	whole milk or milk equivalent
Jersey	1 litre
Ayrshire and Guernsey	1·5 litre
Friesian	2·0 litre

11–28 days

	milk equivalent
Jersey	3·0 litre
Ayrshire and Guernsey	3·5 litre
Friesian	4·5 litre

29–35 days
Reduce milk equivalent by approximately 0·57 litre per day until calf
is weaned on 35th day.

Remarks
Early weaning concentrate mixture (see below) with *good* hay/straw
and water available ad lib from the fifth day.

2. Feeding from sixth to twelfth week
Early weaning concentrate mixture plus good hay/straw and water ad
lib continues to be fed until consumption reaches the following levels:

Jersey	1·8 kg
Ayrshire and Guernsey	2·0 kg
Friesian	2·5 kg

Remarks
(a) Proprietary 'early weaning' pellets (16–18 per cent CP) can be
    purchased, or the following 'early weaning' concentrate can be
    made up:

	per cent
Flaked maize	50
Rolled oats or barley	20
Linseed cake	10
Dried skimmed milk	10
White fishmeal	10

Plus $\frac{1}{2}$–1 per cent of synthetic A and D vitamin supplement.
(b) Good hay or barley straw must be available.
(c) After the 12–14th week the early weaning concentrates can be
    replaced by a concentrate mixture as fed under the 'traditional'
    system, or proprietary calf-rearing pencils can be used.

FEEDING RECOMMENDATIONS

First 4 days—Colostrum.
   5–7 days—50:50 colostrum/milk:acidified milk substitute.
    8 days—Acidified milk substitute.

Weaning-calves need to be fed on acidified milk substitute ad lib for about three weeks; after this, weaning can be carried out on a gradual basis. It needs to be gradual because of the lack of rumen development at this stage, so it should take place over a two-week period. The dry foods, hay and weaning pellets should be available and their intake will increase as the acidified milk substitute is reduced.

The system is successful and popular because:

● It is a simple system to operate.
● There is flexibility of labour—particularly at weekends.
● The calves seem to grow well and show bloom.
● The capital costs are minimal.

The cost is higher than conventional bucket rearing, total feed cost to 12 weeks being £41, as against £33 or 62p/kg gain compared to 53p/kg. This has to be weighed against the advantages listed above.

REARING CALVES AT GRASS

To reduce rearing costs further, spring-born calves (i.e. March-May) can be reared outside on the early-weaning system, shelter being cheaply provided by, say, a straw-bale hut.

A clean pasture (a new ley not previously grazed by cattle) should be chosen and rotational paddock system of grazing adopted, allowing a total area of 0·13 hectare per calf. Grazing can then reduce hay and concentrate consumption to not more than 1·4 kg concentrates and 1·4 kg hay per calf per day.

CALF MANAGEMENT

Certain points in the general management of calves reared on the bucket require special emphasis.

House the newly-born calf in a warm box or pen, well ventilated, but free from draughts; rub well with wisps of hay or straw to prevent chilling and dress the navel before it has dried with tincture of iodine or powdered bluestone (copper sulphate) to prevent any bacterial infection.

Do not over-feed with milk at any one feed, as in nature a calf suckles at least three times daily. Too large a feed of milk means that the amount which is surplus to the capacity of the fourth stomach spills into the rumen or first stomach and putrefies, thus setting up digestive scour.

Milk fed below blood heat may lead to similar trouble except when available ad lib.

Use sterilised feeding buckets and try to encourage the calves to drink as slowly as possible. Feeding buckets with rubber teats have many adherents because they force the calf to swallow slowly, as in suckling. This method reduces the incidence of digestive troubles.

With purchased calves, which have probably suffered a period of starvation, give a first feed of 1·1–1·7 litres warm (38°C) water according to size of calf, to which 113 g of glucose has been added. This helps to satisfy hunger without the risk of digestive scour—milk can then be fed at the next meal.

To combat infectious scours due to *Escherichia coli* infection, a prophylaxis of a proprietary *E. coli* serum can be given by a veterinary surgeon; otherwise, antibiotics such as terramycin or aureomycin can be used under veterinary supervision.

To teach a calf to drink, back it into a corner of its box or pen, with its milk feed in a shallow bowl or small bucket. To make it suck insert one finger of right hand into the calf's mouth and then guide its head so that its mouth is immersed in the milk, holding the bowl or bucket in the left hand.

The calf sucks readily if its head is slightly raised, so at first do not attempt to make it drink with its head down. As the calf sucks and swallows the milk, slowly withdraw the finger so that the calf begins to drink rather than suck.

After the second or third feed, a calf will usually drink from the bucket at head level, without further trouble. Patience is essential.

FEEDING INDIVIDUALLY

If calves are housed in groups feed them individually. Use individual feeding yokes, or tie up each calf with a leather strap at feeding time; and do not release them until their lips have dried, as this will reduce the risk of cross-suckling.

Watch the calves carefully as loss of appetite is a danger signal. It may mean the onset of pneumonia or white scour which are both highly infectious diseases. It may also be the first sign of digestive scour.

Make all changes in the calves' diet as slowly as possible. This principle is indicated in the feeding scheme outlined earlier in this chapter.

Housing for calves need not be elaborate. The main objectives are to keep the young calves warm, provide ample bedding, and to construct interior wall surfaces and floors so thay they can easily be cleaned and disinfected. Wherever possible ample sunlight should be admitted.

After each batch of calves are weaned, the calf-house should be given a thorough cleaning, using 5 per cent proprietary detergent steriliser to remove dirt adhering on walls and fittings. Following this with a short rest of five to seven days is also very beneficial in preventing a build-up of infection in the premises, which can cause severe mortality from scouring or calf diphtheria where rearing is a continuous process. A power wash system is advisable.

Disbudding

Under the Protection of Animals (Anaesthetics) Act of 1964, it is illegal to disbud a calf over seven days old except under an anaesthetic. The standard de-horning method is with the hot iron.

Electrically heated or gas-heated dehorning irons are available. The anaesthetic should be injected to each horn bud at least 15 minutes before using the iron. (The site of injection is critical and it is essential that operators receive qualified instruction).

Disbudding is best carried out at 2–3 weeks of age. The operation becomes progressively harder with increasing age.

EAR-MARKING

When calves are ear-marked in the right ear for registration purposes, it is a good plan to examine them for any extra teats on the udder. At this age, their removal can be easily effected with a pair of sharp curved surgical scissors without the risk of damaging the udder tissues.

Tattooing itself should be done carefully. Try to avoid tattooing across the ear veins, thus avoiding septic ears or indistinct tattoo marks owing to incomplete closure of the forceps. For Friesians a red marking ink shows up best. Ear tags are now approved for ear-marking under the Tuberculosis Order 1964 by the MAFF.

REARING BULL CALVES

As previously noted, bull calves are often reared on the suckling system. There is no reason, however, why pail feeding should not be equally effective, provided the level of feeding is raised some

20–25 per cent higher than with heifer calves. For example, where a heifer calf receives 4·5 litres of whole milk per day, a bull calf should have 5·5 litres. Likewise, where a heifer calf would be fed up to a maximum of 1·8 kg of concentrates, a bull calf should get 2·3 kg.

Feeding a bull calf generously encourages quick growth and enables the animal to be put to service early in life, thus giving an earlier progeny test.

A bull calf may be capable of service before ten months of age, and should consequently be segregated from heifers after weaning.

CASTRATION

The Protection of Animals (Anaesthetics) Act does not permit castration of a calf over three months old without the use of an anaesthetic, and prohibits the use of the rubber ring method (see later) after seven days of age.

Where bull calves are reared for beef, castration usually takes place at from two to eight months of age. The later in life the operation is performed the more masculine the steer develops in appearance. This can be an advantage when selling cattle as stores.

A method of castration much favoured is the Burdizzo Bloodless Castrator. Young calves can be castrated while standing, but those over three months are best castrated lying down.

The operator's assistant should sit on the calf's head and keep the uppermost hind leg of the calf pulled well forward. Before closing the jaws of the castrator make sure that the spermatic cord is between them, and make two independent closures for each cord.

Castration with a knife is very effective and probably more reliable than the bloodless castrator, but is a job for the veterinary surgeon.

The rubber ring method for calves below seven days of age involves application of a rubber ring held open by a pair of special pliers to the scrotum, making sure the immature testicles are through the ring. Closing the pliers and easing off the ring completes the operation.

FEEDING AFTER WEANING

Now comes the question of feeding calves after weaning. It is wise to continue to give from 0·9 to 2·2 kg of concentrates per day from weaning until the calves are eight to nine months old, and relate concentrate feeding to liveweight gain.

Their increasing appetite for food can be met by feeding extra hay, straw or silage.

During this period growing calves will consume from 0·30 kg to 0·45 kg of hay per month of age. Thus a six-month-old Jersey calf should get about 1·8 kg of hay or 5·4 kg of silage, whereas a Friesian calf of similar age should get 2·7 kg of hay or 8·2 kg of silage—in fact bulk feeds are fed ad lib.

It is essential that attention must be given to the calves attaining the target liveweight applicable to their age. If the target is not being reached then the food input must be increased until the deficit is corrected. Care must be taken to ensure that when young stock are housed away from steading, they are observed regularly and a check is made on their progress. A visual appraisal is of course useful but the only sure way to know that cattle are gaining weight as they should is to weigh regularly. Once a month would be ideal.

Young Stock at Grass

Calves are usually turned out to grass at about six months of age by which time they are sufficiently well grown to make the best use of grass. Grazing is attendant with the risk of husk and worm infection, usually more manifest in the autumn months; at the first sign of coughing, give a feed of hay at night and if possible house in a shed or yard to prevent a serious onset of husk.

Experiments in New Zealand with identical twins has shown that calves rotationally grazed on new leys outweigh the opposite twins grazed on low-quality pasture by over 50 kg at ten months old. The old practice of always using a paddock convenient to the buildings as a permanent calf paddock—a common practice on many farms in Britain—cannot be too strongly condemned.

Provided clean grazing is available, calves can be turned out to grass by early April with 0·9–2·2 kg of concentrates per head to maintain nutrient intake for the first three to four weeks. Choose a sheltered field for this purpose. To minimise risk of husk infection a vaccine can be given in two doses one month apart, one month before turnout. This treatment is expensive, but is recommended where the incidence of husk has been high in the past.

On farms where losses from blackleg have occurred, preventive vaccination of all young calves at turning-out time should be carried out.

AGE FOR BULLING

The age for bulling depends upon the breed and also upon the requirement of the desired calving pattern. Certainly the smaller breeds tend to become sexually mature earlier than the larger breeds, but this has to be correlated to the practical demands of the annual milk production cycle.

It is generally suggested that heifers should not calve before twenty-three months old but should calve as soon as possible after that age. In an autumn-calving herd the calving of heifers should be arranged so that animals born in August could calve at twenty-five months old, whereas any animals born in November and December need to be pushed to calve at twenty-three months old, thus preserving the calving pattern.

The majority of herds have calving indices of considerably over 365 days. If heifers are not brought in at the right time then the calving pattern of the whole herd is likely to become rapidly dispersed over the whole of the winter period.

Some degree of block calving should be aimed for as this does simplify certain aspects of herd management.

A BASIC RATION

For a bulling heifer, depending on the breed, the basic ration in winter should be at least 0·9 kg per day concentrated foods, as fed for milk production, the dairy herd ration, or its equivalent in the form of mineralised barley with protein supplement, together with hay/straw at 0·2–0·4 kg per day per month of age. Thus for a Jersey heifer, fifteen months old, feed:

- 3·4 kg hay—or hay equivalent in silage
- 0·9–2·3 kg concentrates
- plus straw to appetite.

And for a Friesian heifer, twenty months old, feed:

- 7 kg of hay (or hay equivalent in silage)
- 0·9–2·3 kg of concentrates
- plus straw to appetite.

These rations would have to be adjusted according to the rate of liveweight gain.

It is undesirable to have heifers in too good a condition in the early stages of pregnancy.

Feeding the In-Calf Heifer

During pregnancy the aim should be steadily to increase condition from the relative leanness of the bulling heifer to the well-conditioned down-calver.

From the fifth month of pregnancy onwards, the demands of the developing foetus and udder rapidly increase. With autumn-calving heifers, this demand on bodily reserves is usually adequately met from the grazing. Spring-calving heifers, however, should be given a winter diet at least equivalent to thirty per cent above their actual maintenance requirements.

Table 16·3 can be taken as a guide.

Table 16.3. Winter Ration for In-Calf Heifers (all in kilograms)

Breed	Liveweight	Basal ration hay	Supplemented by silage or kale	
Jersey	317	4·5	9·5	12·7
Ayrshire/Guernsey	381	5·4	9·5	12·7
Friesian	509	8·2	9·5	12·7

The full hay equivalent could be provided in silage. Where the bulk feed is not of good enough quality, then it may be necessary to feed 1 kg of concentrates to ensure that the heifers attain their target calving weight.

The liveweight gain after the animal has been confirmed in calf should be 0·66 kg per day, based on the following calculation: deducting bulling weight (330 kg) from calving weight (510 kg) gives a gain of 180 kg to be made in 270 days, or 0·66 kg per day.

When in-calf heifers are out to grass and there is sufficient, this should be adequate to maintain the acquired growth rate through the summer. If the grass becomes scarce, then immediate steps should be taken to supplement the ration, so that the animals continue to gain weight as required.

Animals must be brought to calving in a fit but not fat condition.

Use of Urea Supplements

The use of urea as a supplement to barley or oat straw fed ad lib to dairy heifers is now increasingly common. In block form or as liquid formulations, the urea is consumed in small doses over twenty-four hours, thus reducing the risk of excess ammonia being produced in the rumen. Appetite for straw is raised by some forty per cent, but rationing of the straw is not recommended; when fed ad lib the cattle select the most palatable roughage, the residue being used as litter.

Urea supplements, though expensive, do offer the opportunity to use barley straw in place of hay. This reduces the area of grass required to rear replacement heifers, enabling more feed grain to be grown, resulting in greater profit to the farm as a whole and increased productivity by utilisation of arable by-products. It is important to realise the necessity of feeding some rolled barley or other cereal feed when urea feeding is practised.

ECONOMICS OF REARING REPLACEMENTS

In strict economic terms, the rearing of dairy heifers gives a much lower return per hectare than milk production.

An average gross margin per hectare for dairy cows in 1980 was £565, resulting from a yield of five thousand litres at a stocking rate of 2·05 cows per hectare compared to a gross margin per forage hectare of dairy young stock of £209, at a stocking rate equivalent of 1·5 cows per hectare. Higher heifer gross margins per hectare are possible if grazing is intensified and allied to winter feeding systems which have less dependence upon home-produced bulk feeds, hay or silage; but the same is also true of dairy cow gross margins, per hectare.

Home-reared heifers can be justified in various circumstances where the following might apply:

1. Where there is a well-planned breeding policy based on progeny-tested sires, the genetic potential of the herd is improved. If this genetic potential is linked to high levels of production, then obviously there would be an expanding market for surplus stock if the reward for the exercise would be in stock sales at a premium rather than calculated in terms of margin per acre.

2. Where land not suitable for the dairy herd is available for summer grazing.

3. Where wintering can be cheapened by use of straw feeding of arable by-products or labour-saving systems, e.g. self-feeding of silage utilising maximum bulk of feeds rather than early-cut quality silage.

A self-contained herd is, it should be noted, more favourably placed than flying herds to eliminate such diseases as brucellosis and mastitis.

1

DEHORNING A CALF

1 With assistant holding calf in firm grip, feel for groove in skull between eye and horn bud. This contains nerves which run to horn bud and an injection of 4 cc of anaesthetic will 'freeze' them. Hold needle flat against skull and guide point in (away from eye) with your spare thumb withdraw plunger slightly and check for blood. If blood is present pull out and inject again on the other side of the head. Repeat on other side of head.

2 Allow between 5 and 10 minutes for the anaesthetic to take full effect. During this time, clip back hair round horns to expose immature buds. Note how head is held in a bent-neck grip around the thigh.

3 Having heated dehorning iron (see that it gets red hot), apply it squarely, ensuring that bud is fully enclosed in burning ring. Press down iron and rotate it uniformly to speed burning action and shift any build-up of burned material. Burn down until layer of white cartilage is reached, then remove bud with a knife or a flick with iron.

4 A correctly performed operation will leave two clean bud sockets—the skin and skull having been burned but no flesh. Slight bleeding can be stopped by cauterising. If desired, the wound can be dusted with sulphanilamide powder.

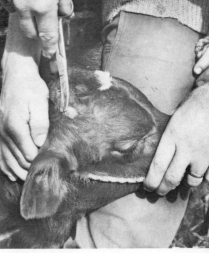

2

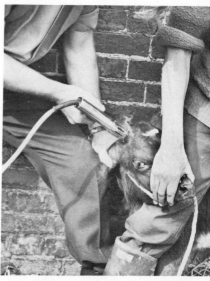

3

4

Above: The equipment needed for ad lib cold milk feeding is cheap and simple Here the calves are sucking through a rack of teats and siphon tubes from insulated containers made out of plastic dustbins.

Left: Use sterilised feeding buckets and try to encourage the calves to drink as slowly as possible.

Left: A calf-rearing shed at the National Institute for Research in Dairying.

Below: Calf cubicles at the Somerset Farm Insitute.

Right: Cold milk feeding of calves at pasture. The feeding apparatus is positioned to offer shelter to suckling calves. Trials at the Grassland Research Institute at Hurley have shown that the health of calves fed on cold milk is in no way inferior to calves fed on warm milk.

For home-bred replacements to be reasonably economic, the two key factors to note are the age of calving, i.e. at two or two and half years, and the stocking rate. Earlier calving and higher stocking rates combine together to give better gross margins per hectare, but stocking rate is the more important factor of the two. The capital required for the 2½-year calving period is greater than for the two-year calving period by something approaching 40 per cent, and this affects the profitability of the unit, particularly if there is any possibility of a cash-flow problem.

CONTROLLED BREEDING—PROSTAGLANDIN

In recent years there has been an increasing interest in the technique of breeding heifers to fit into a planned calving pattern.

This involved the use of prostaglandin, a naturally produced substance in the body which can be artificially produced and used for controlled breeding.

In a normal cow reproduction cycle, a corpus luteum is formed which will be retained if a pregnancy is established or sometimes as a physiological malfunction. An injection of prostaglandin will remove the corpus luteum and allows oestrous to occur, usually within 7 days.

If used on a number of cows with functional corpora lutea their synchronisation of oestrous is possible. Cows can then be organised to fit into a planned calving pattern. This technique, however, is no substitute for good husbandry and breeding practice. With heifers, prostaglandin can be used in a two-injection system. The first injection is followed by a second one 11 days later. The heifers must be inseminated or served at 72 and 96 hours after the second injection. Service may also be carried out on observed oestrous after the first injection.

A simple timetable for the two injection system would be: 1st injection—eleven days later 2nd injection 10 am—serve three days later at 10 am and next day at 10 am. It must be understood that heifers must be well grown and in good condition for successsful mating. If this is not the case, good results even with drugs are by no means assured. It is also very important that animals must be cycling regularly for success to be achieved.

BRUCELLOSIS ERADICATION SCHEME

Brucellosis in cattle is a contagious diesease which may cause abortion; in many cases it causes infertility and it certainly leads to reduced milk yields.

The Brucellosis (Accredited Herds) Scheme was initiated in 1967 by the Ministry of Agriculture. Eventually the intention was to establish brucellosis-freed herds over the country. Eradication of brucellosis commenced in November 1971 on a voluntary basis, but in three main areas of Britain it was made compulsory by November 1972, and since that time further areas have been included in the compulsory scheme. The last eradication areas in Scotland and England were scheduled to start in the compulsory scheme in November 1979.

The use of the S.19 vaccine is prohibited within attested areas and by October 1979 all vaccine was withdrawn from the remainder of the country.

To reach accredited status a herd was obliged to pass three consecutive blood tests. Accredited herds are tested periodically by the Ministry of Agriculture to ensure that they remain free from the disease. Dairy herds are also tested by the Marketing Boards on a monthly basis and any failures are communicated to the Ministry. If there is an abortion at any time, again this information has to be communicated to the Ministry. Where animals prove to be reactors, there is a compulsory slaughter policy; compensation is paid by the Ministry.

CHAPTER 17

DISEASE IN DAIRY HERDS

A National Committee reported many years ago that 12 per cent of total annual production was lost every year by British dairy farmers through disease in the dairy herds. Tuberculosis has been eliminated and the campaign to eliminate brucellosis is almost completed, but mastitis remains a serious disease to dairy herds.

To reduce losses attributable to disease and to promote positive health and longevity in dairy stock should be a cardinal principle in dairy herd management. Disease makes for uneconomic production and renders any breeding programme incapable of realisation.

FOUR MANAGEMENT RULES

It is not possible to give in one chapter of a book all that a dairy farmer should know about cattle diseases and their control and treatment. Readers are referred to the appropriate textbooks for such details. Nevertheless, I do want to discuss here how enlightened herd management can prevent disease.

A good stockman should:

- Be capable of detecting the early symptoms of ill-health in dairy cattle.

- Take steps to eliminate the sources of disease on the farm— whether from contaminated water supplies, infected buildings or pastures.

- Enlist the aid of the veterinary profession to control disease by suitable preventive measures.

- Adopt all management practices which will reduce the risk of disease.

Signs of Ill-Health

A mental picture of the cow in good health is a valuable attribute of good stockmanship, and the following guide is suggested to help in the detection of ill-health and prompt treatment.

The general posture of the cow, her movements, breathing and behaviour should be normal. Warning symptoms which may be exhibited by the cow include standing with her head down, showing undue lassitude or a tendency to separate from the herd.

Her appetite should be normal. If it is not, make sure the cause is not unsuitable food, dirty feeding troughs or lack of water.

The skin, which should be handled over the last rib, should feel soft and pliable. A tight hide and a lack of bloom often accompanies digestive troubles or feverish conditions.

Nostrils should be moist and free of mucus; the eyes should be full, not sunken, and free of a fixed or staring look which often accompanies the onset of milk fever.

The dung should be reasonably formed, and obviously affected by diet; it should be free from gas bubbles as in Johne's disease or liverfluke.

Constipation or scouring should be particularly noted. The vulva and tail should show no evidence of coloured disharge from the genital organs; a clear discharge is a sign of the normal reproductive cycle; pus-containing discharges indicate a septic condition.

Urine should be a straw-coloured. If it is darker, lighter or contains blood, urinary tract infection should be suspected.

Any fall in milk yield indicates that the animal is suffering from an interference in her metabolic processes such as wire in the rumen, displaced abomasum or any disease accompanied by a high temperature. Abnormal smells are indicative of acetonaemia or aromatic feeding agents, such as kale or turnips.

When a cow seems off-colour, take her temperature by inserting a clinical thermometer into the rectum. Normal temperature is 38·8°–39°C. With the index finger of the right hand also take the pulse rate by pressing on the artery at the base of the tail. Normal rate is 60 per minute.

Diagnosis

The full diagnosis of disease is, of course, the veterinary surgeon's job, but the following list of symptoms and the diseases with which they are associated will form a useful guide for stockmen:

Symptom	Associate with:
Loss of appetite	In calves: (a) scours (b) virus pneumonia (c) joint ill (d) any other infection causing a high temperature In cows: (a) mastitis (b) wire (c) pneumonia (d) displaced abomasum (e) any condition causing a high temperature
Depraved appetite	Suspect mineral deficiency or lack of some dietary constituent
High temperature	(a) pneumonia (b) acute mastitis (c) peritonitis
Low temperature	(a) terminal condition following any of above (b) milk fever (c) toxic mastitis
Unsteady gait	(a) milk fever (b) staggers (c) tetanus
Skin tight, lacking bloom	Any condition causing scouring (a) worm infestation (b) liver fluke (c) corn poisoning (d) Johne's disease
Constipation, faeces hard and solid	(a) improper feeding, excess fibre (b) acetonaemia (c) many feverish conditions
Diarrhoea	(a) worm infestation, liver fluke (b) improper feeding, minimal fibre (c) Johne's disease
Milk abnormal clots or pus in fore-milk, udder induration may be present	Chronic mastitis
Milk yield greatly reduced udder hot and painful, pus in milk, temperature high, udder induration present	Acute mastitis

Discharges from vulva
- (i) clear slime
- (ii) pus present and foetid smell, fertility impaired
- (iii) white discharge fertility likely impaired

Indicative of normal reproduction cycle
Retained afterbirth if recently calved or abortion occurred
Chronic inflammation of the womb or vagina
Infectious bovine rhinotracheitis (IBR)

Lameness

- (a) foul in the foot—infection between claws
- (b) foot rot
- (c) traumatic penetration of horn
- (d) hereditary factors producing soft horn or malformed feet
- (e) concrete—newly laid
- (f) joint or navel ill in calves.

If accompanied by profuse salivation

suspect (a) foot and mouth disease.
(b) IBR

Abnormal heat periods

- (a) cystic ovaries
  nymphomaniac condition
  persistent bulling
- (b) persistent corpus luteum no heat observed
- (c) infection following cleansing metritis/abortion/retained
- (d) IBR

Abnormal smell to breath or milk

Suspect acetonaemia if a sickly and penetrating smell.

Abnormal smell plus loss of apetite

- (a) wire
- (b) displaced abomasum

Laboured breathing

- (a) Pneumonia should be suspected.
- (b) IBR

Loss of cud, profuse salivation

Examine for abnormal teeth; wooden tongue or jumpy jaw; foot and mouth disease

Bloodstained urine

Redwater or kidney inflammation

Blood in milk

Suspect burst blood vessel

Failure to come on heat

- (a) seasonal—late winter
- (b) nutritional—energy deficit
- (c) persistent corpus luteum
- (d) metritis
- (e) poor observation
- (f) IBR

Unable to rise

- (a) milk fever
- (b) injury to spine during calving
- (c) damage to pelvis during physical riding

Swollen joints	(a) navel ill, joint ill
	(b) foul in the foot, physical damage
Persistent coughing, loss of condition	Suspect worm or husk infestation, house immediately, feed generously, dose on veterinary advice.

SEEK VETERINARY ADVICE

Any obviously sick animal should be put in a well-littered loose-box as soon as observed. If the temperature is abnormal, keep the patient warm—if necessary by rugging up—and feed on a laxative and nutritious diet: for example, bran mashes with a little linseed cake to increase palatability.

If there is any doubt as to what ails the animal, call in veterinary advice and act upon it.

CLEAN UP DISEASE SOURCES

The importance of eradicating sources of infection has been stressed. Water supplies, if allowed to become contaminated with urine or faeces, are a potent source of disease. With dairy cattle piping water supply and fencing off all open pools will pay handsome dividends.

Buildings should be conscientiously spring-cleaned as an annual routine. Walls and floors should be rendered with a smooth surface cement finish and woodwork replaced, where practicable, with tubular steel fittings. All cement facing and floors and all metal fittings should be scrubbed thoroughly during the spring-clean with washing soda added to the water at the rate of 1 kg washing soda in 100 kg water. Any woodwork is best either creosoted or disinfected with a blow-lamp. Sunlight is the enemy of most disease organisms—let it in wherever you can.

Pastures should not be consistently over-grazed with cattle. If heavy stocking is obtained by strip grazing, then alternate the grazing with cutting to reduce the risk of parasitic infection.

Remember, too, the advantages of mixed grazing in this respect.

DOSING AGAINST WORMS

Dosing of young cattle with an anthelmintic is recommended in early July and ten days after housing in the autumn (allowing immature worms to develop and be killed). Between these two periods, it is necessary to dose as stocking rate and condition of pasture dictate. Parasitic infection of cattle is more common than is generally realised. Again it leads to a low resistance and allows other diseases to get a hold on the stock. Husk (parasitic bronchitis) can be treated in the same way as worms, by controlling the animals' environmental conditions. Prevention is better than cure; an oral vaccine is recommended before turning out to grass.

The Cow's Reproductive Cycle

The control of disease in the dairy cow obviously plays an important role in achieving a satisfactory level of quality milk. As levels of production are increasing so the particular importance of regular breeding in the dairy cow has become recognised.

It is essential that a cow should produce a calf each year, that is, that it should have a calving interval of something approaching 365 days. To achieve this kind of breeding regularity it is fundamental that every dairyman must understand the principles of the cow reproductive cycle.

An outline of the basic cycle is as follows:

1. The cow has two ovaries which release an egg on a 21-day cycle. The egg development and release is connected with the presence of the follicle stimulating hormone (FSH) produced in the pituitary gland.

   This follicle produces Oestrogen, present in the egg, which is responsible for the signs of heat shown by the cow; it also prepares the uterus for the eventual reception of the fertilised egg. The egg is fertilised on its way to the uterus from the ovary, by way of the connecting tube, the oviduct.

2. The departure of the egg from the ovary leaves a cavity which is filled by the rapidly growing Yellow Body or Corpus Luteum.

3. As it grows, the corpus luteum secretes the hormone Progesterone which has three important functions.

   - Its presence in the cow's bloodstream is necessary for the maintenance of pregnancy.

   - A high level of progesterone will prevent cows coming on heat, i.e. prevents oestrous. This is the reason why cows which are pregnant do not not come on heat.

   - If the released egg is not fertilised it will then pass out of the cow's reproductive tract and so the corpus luteum will contract; the level of progesterone falls and the next period of heat begins.

This brings the reproductive cycle round full circle in 21 days.

4. With the decline of the corpus luteum, the ovary begins to develop a swelling, described as a follicle, which contains the next egg to be released.

In a normally well-fed and well-managed dairy cow the reproductive cycle continues at the 21-day interval until such time as the fertilisation of the released egg is effected by service and pregnancy commences.

The successful functioning of the cow's reproductive cycle is dependent upon a highly complex balance of hormones in the bloodstream which is considerably affected by the quality of cow nutrition and management. The highest proportion of cows culled from an average herd are sent off because of their failure to breed regularly. In many cases this may not be the result of the cow's genetic ability to breed, but is due to a failure in the nutrition and a general lack of understanding or management of the cow's reproductive cycle.

<h3 style="text-align:center">MONITORING LOW FERTILITY</h3>

This should be a basic operation of dairy husbandry and one area where theoretical knowledge must be linked to practical application. Low fertility must be recorded on a day-to-day basis; each cow acts independently from all other cows in the herd and so information on its particular breeding cycle must be recorded and acted upon. Breeding records must be kept. On many farms this takes the form of a Breeding Board, of which there are several types, both round and square. The following basic details need to be recorded, assuming of course that a 365-day calving interval is the desired objective.

1. After calving, all cows should be regularly observed and the dates when they were on heat recorded in their individual records. This must be done even if there is no intention of serving a cow. It is so important to establish the fact that the cow is cycling regularly.

2. If a cow is expected to calve once per year (every 365 days), given a pregnancy period of approximately 280 days the animal must be put in calf, i.e. served, within the first 85 days (three months) from calving. In practical terms this means effective service at the second or third heat period.

3. After service, it is vital to note whether any cow returns on heat, indicating that the previous service was not successful.

Individual cows returning on a regular basis would warrant veterinary examination.

4. If cows are not seen on heat after service it cannot be assumed that they are in-calf. In the interest of efficient dairy management it is advisable to have all served cows pregnancy-tested by a veterinary surgeon. This would usually be carried out about six to eight weeks after service. Some vets with large dairy practices become very skilled at this operation and can successfully confirm pregnancies as early as five weeks.

5. Once pregnancy has been confirmed, eventual due date and drying-off date can be established; in this way, breeding performance can be monitored as it occurs in early lactation.

To emphasise the importance of this subject of herd fertility, it would be interesting to see how a good herd with a high level of 7,000 litre average and a calving index of 420 days, only looks like an average herd when the yield is corrected to a 365-day calving index.

$$\text{i.e.} \quad \frac{7,000}{420} \times 365 = 6,083 \text{ litres}$$

Calf numbers per year are also considerably reduced if the index exceeds 365 days.

When cows fail to breed, the possible causes must be investigated as soon as possible.

Low Production Life

In this country, at present short of beef, a longer milking life in those breeds of dairy cattle with no beef-producing qualities should be made an objective as important as high production per lactation. It is a disturbing fact that only about 8 per cent of recorded cows survive until the fifth to seventh lactation when production is at its maximum.

Various surveys of the extent of the replacement of dairy cows in milk-recorded herds have indicated an annual turnover of from 20 to 25 per cent. This means that, on average, a cow is in the herd for only four or five years. Yet herds are known where average working life of cows is seven or more years.

This relatively high rate is due, to a considerable extent, to losses from diseases such as those discussed earlier. They amount to at least 50 per cent of the total disposals. Losses through accidents and through deaths not directly attributable to disease are no more than 20 per cent, and disposals on account of poor milking ability amount to roughly the same.

To reduce herd wastages we therefore need:

- A better level of management to reduce the incidence of diseases and a greater disease consciousness on the part of stockmen, particularly in regard to infertility problems.
- Better breeding policies so that the general productivity of home-reared replacements reaches a higher level.
- Greater attention to the welfare of the individual cow to reduce the risk of accidents and to maintain the cow in a fit condition over a long and useful working life.

In this last respect, several points are worth emphasising. Many cows break down as milk producers through the stockman's failure to attend to their feet; hoof trimming should be a regular routine in dairy herds whenever necessary.

Value of a Footbath

Where lameness in cows is a recurring problem, it is probable that germs causing necrosis of the foot tissues are being picked up in muddy gateways or at drinking trough surrounds.

To combat this trouble a shallow footbath through which the cows can be driven should be constructed. If the bath is filled with a solution of 5% formalin and the cows are walked through it once a week, the trouble should be cleared up.

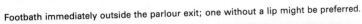

Footbath immediately outside the parlour exit; one without a lip might be preferred.

The bath should be kept covered when not in use; otherwise rainwater will dilute the disinfectant.

WARBLE FLY CONTROL

The Warble Fly (Dressing of Cattle) Order 1936, required all cattle to be compulsorily dressed between 15 March and 30 June to kill the warble larvae in the localised swellings which appear on the backs of infested cattle at this time.

Two further lines of attack against the warble fly are:

● dressing the backs of all cattle (other than cows in milk) with a phosphorus-type insecticide in November or in the spring;
● using an oral type of insecticide at the same time of year.

Both these methods rely on destruction of the warble-fly larvae during their migratory phase in the tissue of the body. These methods should prove a boon for controlling infection in young stock, whether for beef or milk.

Suitable warble-fly dressings and anti-lice powders can be purchased from veterinary chemists.

IBR: INFECTIOUS BOVINE RHINOTRACHEITIS (COW FLU OR RED NOSE)

This is a highly infectious disease which is becoming increasingly prevalent. It is caused by a virus and can result in

(a) Respiratory Disease

(b) Abortion

(c) Encephalitis in young calves

(d) Vulvovaginitis.

All ages and breeds are susceptible but it is mainly seen in cattle over 6 months of age and is probably more common in beef animals and during the winter months. This is due to the fact that the animals are housed, and spread by droplets is more likely. The symptoms are fever, conjunctivitis with lacrimation and salivation. Sometimes an accompanying pneumonia may be present and is usually associated with a secondary bacterial infection.

The disease itself can be severe and the resulting loss of milk, flesh, losses through abortion and the high cost of treatment make it a disease of increasing economic importance. Recently an intra-nasal vaccine has been produced which is highly effective even in the face of an outbreak. Duration of the vaccine is in doubt; animals should be vaccinated annually just before housing.

Disease in the National Dairy Herd

The incidence of disease in the national dairy herd of Great Britain as revealed by a recent survey carried out by the Ministry of Agriculture is summarised in Table 17.1.

Table 17.1. Estimated Incidence of the Various Diseases in the National Dairy Herd

Diseases	Estimated incidence (per cent)
1. Diseases associated with parturition: difficult calving, stillbirth, abortion, retained placenta, other general diseases.	11
2. Infectious diseases: mastitis (acute, mild, summer), winter scours, Johne's disease, others.	15
3. Non-infectious diseases: milk fever, acetonaemia, grass tetany, bloat, traumatic conditions, lameness, other conditions.	17

This survey reveals that 43 per cent of the national dairy herd is at any one time affected by disease of one sort or another; the non-infectious diseases and parturition problems are a challenge to our management, as has been emphasised in this chapter.

CHAPTER 18

PROFITABILITY IN MILK PRODUCTION

THE main purpose of this chapter is to review the factors which determine the profitability of milk production.*

These factors can be divided into three groups. These are:

(1) the economic and political climate;
(2) the agricultural and physical characteristics of individual farms;
(3) the differences in the systems of husbandry and management practices adopted.

ECONOMIC AND POLITICAL FACTORS

The economic and political factors of this country, and in more recent times of the other EEC countries, influence and determine the price the dairy farmer receives for his milk, the price he pays for purchased feeds, and the cost of other inputs such as labour and machinery. The individual farmer has very little influence on these factors and there is relatively little he can do about them on his own. There are, however, national organisations working on his behalf such as the National Farmers Union and the Milk Marketing Board. It is to organisations such as these that he has to turn to and give his support if he wishes to seek more favourable milk price-to-cost ratios.

An examination in depth of these national and international factors is not the main purpose of this chapter. It has to be stressed, however, that the success or otherwise of government policy and

*Obviously this cannot be considered in great detail in the space allowed here and for more extensive discussion readers should refer to *Dairy Farm Business Management* by Slater and Throup, published by Farming Press.

the influence or otherwise dairy farmers have on this policy has a very considerable effect on the profitability of milk production.

Factors Determining Milk Price

Historically milk production has been one of the most profitable enterprises in British farming. Generally it is regarded as more profitable than beef and sheep production and it accounts for a very significant proportion of the total national farm output.

Prior to entry into EEC in 1973 the price of milk and hence the profitability of dairy farming was very dependent on the proportion of milk being used in the liquid, i.e. retail milk market as opposed to the less profitable manufactured market, particularly butter. Manufactured milk could be, and was, imported at low prices. Consequently any substantial expansion in milk production above the liquid market requirements led to a significant fall in producers' returns. Government policy at that time was largely based on the liquid milk market and the concept of 'Standard Quantities' became established. If production exceeded the standard quantity, the price received by producers fell due to the low price received for manufactured milk.

Since our entry into EEC the import of milk products at low world market prices has not been possible due to the EEC system of levies on imports. The price received for milk used for manufacture has increased and this has allowed the home production of milk to be increased without any substantial fall in prices.

These trends are illustrated by information taken from the 1980 edition of *Dairy Facts & Figures* a publication produced annually by the Milk Marketing Board.

Over the period since 1954 there has been very little increase in the amount of milk sold liquid, as can be seen from Table 18.1. Liquid sales in 1974–5 were 13 per cent more than they were twenty years earlier but this increase has fallen back to 5 per cent by 1979–80.

Sales for manufacture in 1979–80 were 189 per cent of those in 1969–70, but liquid sales decreased over the same period by 3 per cent. Manufactured sales account for 50 per cent of total production in 1979–80 compared to 19 per cent in 1954–5, and 34 per cent in 1969–70.

Due to the change in market support arrangement the increase in the price received for manufactured milk between 1969–70 and 1979–80 was 454 per cent, whereas the increase in the average net price received by producers for all milk supplies was only 221 per cent.

Table 18.1. Utilisation of Milk Produced off Farms in England and Wales

Year	Liquid (million litres)	(per cent)	Manufacturing (million litres)	(per cent)	Total (million litres)
1954–55	6103	81	1413	19	7516
1959–60	6253	77	1923	23	8175
1964–65	6647	73	2398	27	9044
1969–70	6664	66	3358	34	10,022
1974–75	6878	62	4273	38	11,115
1979–80	6432	51	6432	49	12,774
74–75 as a percentage of 54–55	113		302		148
79–80 as a percentage of 54–75	105		439		170
79–80 as a percentage of 69–70	97		189		127

Table 18.2. Net Price Receipts

Year	Average net price received by wholesale producers (pence per litre)	Average price received for manufactured milk (pence per litre)
1964–65	3·403	2·038
1969–70	3·548	1·992
1974–75	6·245	5·017
1979–80	11·407	11·026
79–80 as a percentage of 69–70	321	554

A similar expansion in output has taken place throughout the EEC and by the end of the 1970s the EEC as a whole had a surplus of milk products. These surpluses are now an embarrassment and their removal is one of the main problems facing policy-makers in the 1980s.

Although the EEC as a whole is in surplus this is not the case so far as the British market is concerned. British farms only produce about 70 per cent of the national requirements, 30 per cent still being imported. Whether or not this shortfall in home supplies is to be met by an expansion of home production or by imports is the centre of political debate at the present time (1980). The answers have important repercussions for British dairy farming during the 1980s and will largely determine its profitability relative to other enterprises.

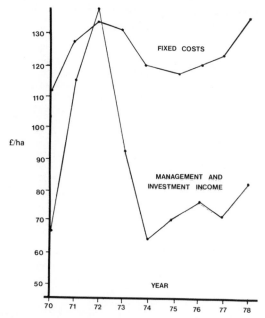

Fixed costs and management income in real terms for dairy farms (1971–78).

The possible continued change in the market outlet, i.e. towards a greater proportion going into manufacture, also has implications from a milk composition point of view. As the proportion going into manufacture increases so does the significance of the butterfat and solids-not-fat content of the milk. This led to an introduction by the Milk Marketing Board in May 1980 of a new quality payments systems.

Even more revolutionary revisions have been suggested to the payments system as for example by the Centre for Agricultural Strategy at Reading University (see *Strategy for the U.K. Dairy Industry*, CAS Report No. 4).

The increase in the proportion of milk used for manufacturing purposes is a major reason for the introduction in 1982–3 of stiffer penalties for milk contaminated with antibiotics. Milk contaminated with antibiotics at only a very small level leads to very substantial losses in manufacture, particularly in cheese-making.

Considerable stress is placed at the present time (1981) on the need for farmers to pay more attention to marketing. Dairy farmers for many years have been fortunate to be able to concentrate on the job of producing milk and leave the job of marketing to the Milk Marketing Board. Hopefully this state of affairs will continue in the future but the milk producer must heed the market and price signals coming from the board. These are expected to place more emphasis on the need for high butterfat and possibly less emphasis on winter milk production. The producer needs to heed these signals and alter his production methods accordingly.

Attention up to now has been focused on factors determining the milk price. Economic and political factors also determine the price received by a dairy farmer for his main by-products, i.e. cull cows and calves. These prices can fluctuate widely from year to year due to variations in the profitability of beef production. The significance of the income from these two sources is often under-estimated. Periods of hardship for dairy farmers tend to coincide with periods of low profitability in beef production, e.g. in 1974–5. Similarly periods of prosperity tend to coincide, e.g. 1972–3.

This variation in the profitability of dairy farmers from year to year was very much a feature of the 1970s, as can be seen from the Graph on page 256 derived from an ICI report on dairy farming.

During the 1970s it was not possible to answer the question 'How profitable is dairy farming?' without specifying the year. Results from one year were not a good guide to results that could be expected in the following year. This high degree of uncertainty is likely to continue in the 1980s due to the disappearance of so-called guaranteed prices and the return to prices based on a market economy.

The Costs of Feed and Labour

Of great importance to each dairy farmer is the general relationship between milk price and the two most important cost items, i.e. feed and labour.

Attention will be drawn later to such factors as 'Margin over Concentrates' as measures of efficiency. At this stage attention is drawn to the relationship between milk price per litre and purchased concentrate costs per tonne or per kilogram.

Under 'normal circumstances', i.e. periods in which dairy farming is relatively profitable this ratio is approximately 1:1, i.e. 1 litre of milk has the same value as 1 kg of concentrates. Or, to put it another way, if the milk price is 12·5 pence per litre, then one would expect the cost of concentrates to be 12·5 pence per kilogram or £125 per tonne. This is a simple but very important rule-of-thumb assessment of one of the most important factors affecting the profitability of milk production at a particular point in time.

If the price of milk is equal to or greater than the cost of concentrates, then the period tends to be profitable as in 1972–3; if it is significantly less, then it tends to be unprofitable as in 1974–75.

The relationship between milk price and feed costs per tonne in recent years is given in Table 18.3.

Table 18.3. Milk Price and Feed Costs

	Milk price (£)	Concentrate costs per kilogram (£)	Ratio
1974–75	6·245	7·82	1 : 1·25
1975–76	7·816	8·02	1 : 1·03
1976–77	9·269	10·03	1 : 1·08
1977–78	9·827	11·06	1 : 1·13
1978–79	10·430	11·26	1 : 1·08
1979–80	11·407	12·91	1 : 1·13

(*Dairy Facts and Figures, 1979*)

Whilst discussing rule of thumb feed cost ratios mention can also be made of a simple yardstick for calf prices. If the price of beef cattle per live kilogram begins to approach the price of barley per tonne good calf prices can be expected, e.g. if beef prices are in excess of 90 pence per kilogram when barley is £100 per tonne.

We now turn to the relationship between milk prices and wages (Table 18.4). Over the past twenty-five years there has been a considerable increase in wages relative to milk prices. 810 litres were needed in 1979–80 to pay one man's weekly wage compared to 262 litres in 1954–5. This trend is expected to continue, probably at an accelerated pace: 1000 litres will probably be needed to pay one man's wages in the 1980s.

Wage costs per litre have not risen at the same rate because mechanisation and building investments have reduced the number of man-hours required per cow. Many farmers, however, have not been able to afford the cost of modernisation and have given up milk production. As a result of these and other factors the number of milk producers in England and Wales fell by 70 per cent between 1954–5 and 1979–80 (see Table 18.5). Similar trends took place in Scotland and Northern Ireland.

Table 18.4 Milk Price and Wages

Year	Milk price (per litre)	Weekly average total earnings* and hours of hired, regular full-time adult male dairy cowmen in Great Britain (£)	(hours)	No. litres equivalent to weekly earnings
1954–55	3·326	8·72	57·1	262
1959–60	3·220	11·64	56·9	361
1964–65	3·403	15·15	56·4	445
1969–70	3·548	20·63	54·8	581
1974–55	6·245	45·03	53·2	721
1978–79	10·430	78·64	53·4	754
1979–80	11·407	92·42	53·2	810
1980–81	12·50†	112†	53	896†

* Source, MAFF, DAFS
†Estimates

Table 18.5. Milk Producers

Year	No. producers	No. Dairy cows (000s)	No. Cows per producer	Yield per cow (litres)
1955	142,792	2415	17	3065
1960	123,137	2595	21	3320
1965	100,449	2650	26	3545
1970	80,265	2714	34	3755
1975	60,279	2701	45	4070
1979	46,972	2734	58	4745
1980	43,358	2627	60	4810
1979 as a percentage of 1955	30	109	353	157

(*Dairy Facts and Figures, 1980*)

Cow numbers throughout this period have remained fairly constant and the average number of cows per producer has increased from 17 to 60.

In 1979 12·4 per cent of producers had 100 cows or more and these 12·4 per cent owned 33·4 per cent of the total number of cows. At the other end of the scale 30·2 per cent producers had less than thirty cows and owned 9·2 per cent of the total.

**Table 18.6. Dairy Herd Size Distribution in
England and Wales, 1979**

Herd size	Percentage of total producers	Percentage of total cows
Less than 30	30·2	9·2
30–49	25·4	17·7
50–99	32·0	39·7
100 and over	12·4	33·4
	100	100

(*Dairy Facts & Figures 1980*, MMB)

This concentration of milk production into the hands of fewer producers carried on just as quickly in the 1970s as in the 1960s. The fall in the 1960s was 35 per cent; the number in 1980 compared to 1970 was down by 46 per cent.

A similar reduction in the 1980s would result in a fall in the number of producers to 27,000 and an increase in the average herd size to 100 by 1990. Whether or not this will happen is debatable. One factor that could mitigate against such a change is the ability of the very large producer to continue to modernise and update his equipment to keep paid labour costs at a reasonable level. On the other hand those farmers with less than thirty cows could find it difficult to survive. A significant reduction in their number would result in an average herd size of 100 without the need for any large expansion in the number of producers with more than 100 cows.

AGRICULTURAL AND PHYSICAL CHARACTERISTICS OF THE
INDIVIDUAL FARM

Reference has already been made to the substantial increase in the size of the average herd. Many small producers have been forced to give up milk production and this trend is expected to continue. The very small farmer often has inherent disadvantages in terms of buildings and other fixed equipment. Consequently he is uncompetitive from a labour productivity point of view.

The availability or otherwise of suitable buildings and fixed equipment is, however, a major factor affecting the viability of a dairy enterprise irrespective of the size of the farm.

In this context it needs to be noted that the rent payable for a farm at any particular point in time or its equivalent, i.e. interest charges on borrowed capital, often does not reflect the adequacy or otherwise of the fixed equipment and buildings. The 'rent equivalent' reflects many factors but the most important is often the length of time the farm has been rented or owned; the longer this period the lower the rent equivalent tends to be. Consequently a farm with a high rent equivalent may have poor buildings and fixed equipment whereas a farm with a relatively low rent equivalent may have good fixed equipment and buildings. Young farmers in particular are faced with this problem. To overcome it they have to be prepared to accept a lower level of personal wages from their farm than they would receive as hired workers doing the same work.

The lack of adequate buildings and fixed equipment tends to result in higher than average labour costs. This can be overcome by making the appropriate investments, but in the short term this leads to a substantial financial burden being placed on the business. This makes the business less competitive compared to established neighbouring businesses even though it may be just as well or better managed.

The lack of good buildings, good milking premises and good services such as water and electricity is considered to have been one of the main reasons for producers giving up milk production during the past twenty-five years. It is also considered that this factor will continue to be of vital importance in the future.

The quality and nature of the land is also a significant factor in milk production, but the significance of this factor is sometimes overestimated. The milk producer at high altitude in the North with a short grass-growing season obviously has a handicap compared to a lowland farmer in the South-West. Many costings, however, have shown that differences in location are not the most significant factors determining the difference in profit between individual farms. Profits achieved in one part of the country do not differ significantly from those in another. There is a trend, however, for dairy farmers to become more concentrated in the West of the country compared to the East. This reflects in part the ability of farms in the East to make good profits out of arable farming.

HUSBANDRY AND MANAGEMENT FACTORS

A feature of all economic surveys of milk production is the very wide variation in profits between individual farms. These differences are found even when the surveys are restricted to small geographical areas and to farms carrying out similar systems of husbandry, e.g. all producing milk from Friesian cows on a silage-based feeding system.

Considerable discussion takes place as to which is the best system of producing milk, but the first question a dairy farmer or herdsman should ask is, 'Am I getting the best I can out of my present system?' He should follow up with 'If not, what can I do about it?' rather than looking to a new system to solve his problems.

In this section it is necessary to quote costs and returns to highlight the significance of various factors. This immediately causes problems:

● Financial results differ considerably from year to year as has already been mentioned so the figures shown may not be normal.
● We are living in a period of rapid inflation and costs quoted today are out of date within a very short time, in fact they are often out of date by the time they are published.

Financial data quoted in this book is almost certain to be out of date by the time it reaches the reader. It should be used therefore not as a guide to actual levels of profit that can be achieved, but to indicate the main factors that determine the profit level.

Figures provided jointly by the MAFF and the MMB for the years ended 31 March 1977, 1978, 1979 and 1980 are shown in Table 18.7.

Attention is drawn to the following points:

1. Feed costs account for a high proportion i.e. approximately 60 per cent of total costs, and purchased feed costs in turn account for a large proportion of the total feed costs.

2. The profit margin in 1977–8 is 174 per cent of that achieved in the previous year. The milk price rose in 1977–8 compared to 1976–7. There were increases in labour and other costs *but* purchased feed costs fell and there was a substantial increase in the calf value, i.e. favourable movements in the feed cost/milk price ratio and in the price of calves resulted in a profitable year compared to 1976–7.

3. Milk and calf values increased again in 1978–9 but these increases were not sufficient to offset the substantial increase in feed, labour and other costs, giving a reduction in profit of 5 per cent.

4. The profit fell by a further 17 per cent in 1979–80. Total costs were up by 16 per cent compared to the previous year but milk returns were only up by 10 per cent.

Table 18.7. Results per Cow

	1976–77 £	1977–78 £	1978–79 £	1979–80 £
Milk returns	419	472	514	564
Calf value	28	37	52	52
	447	509	566	617
Less herd replacement cost	14	22	27	21
Gross output	433	487	539	596
Costs				
Feed—purchased	156	147	161	190
—homegrown	51	52	68	78
—grazing	32	39	45	52
	239	238	274	320
Labour	62	64	74	85
Other costs	75	86	97	112
Total	376	388	445	517
PROFIT MARGIN	57	99	94	78
Yield (litres)	4396	4701	4819	4854
Milk price	9·53p	10·04p	10·67p	11·63p

It should also be noted that the *real* drop in the profit is greater than shown as the profit figures are not adjusted for the fall in the value of the pound sterling, i.e. for inflation.

5. Account has not been taken in these costings of the increase in dairy cow unit values between April 1976 and April 1980. The increase over this period was in the region of £160 per cow, or approximately £40 per annum. *Note.* The value of the dairy cow as a hedge against inflation is a point not be forgotten when comparing milk production profits to those obtained from arable farming.

We now need to look in more detail at the factors determining the level of profit and in particular at those a farmer can influence by his management and production efficiency.

The average results a dairy farmer can expect to achieve at 1980–1 cost/price levels are set out in the Table 18.8. Note that these are budget figures and are set out in such a way as to allow the reader to update them at current cost/price levels.

Table 18.8. Budget Results

	1980–81 Prices	Per cow £	Current prices	Per cow
Milk sales	5000 litres @ 12·0p	600	litres @	
less concentrate feed costs	5000 litres @ 4·0p	200*	litres	
MARGIN OVER CONCENTRATES	5000 litres @ 8·0p	400		
		45		
add Calf value	95 per cent @ £50		% @	
		445		
subtract Herd maintenance cost	25 per cent @ £140	35	% @	
		410		
subtract	£		£	
Veterinary fees, medicines	10			
AI, recording, dairy expenses	20			
Bedding	5	35		
GROSS MARGIN before forage costs		375		
Forage costs	0.5 ha @ £120	60	ha @ £	
GROSS MARGIN		315		
less FIXED COSTS				
Labour	150% £66·70**	100		
Power and machinery	0·5 ha @ £160†	80	@	
Sundry overheads	0.5 ha @ £40‡	20	@	
		200		
PROFIT before rent, finance & management charges		115		
Rent	0.5 ha @ £60	30	@	
MANAGEMENT AND INVESTMENT INCOME		85		

* 1·6 tonne (0·32 kg per litre) concentrate equivalent @ £125 per tonne.
** Weekly wage rate for craftsmen, Agricultural Wages Order January 1980. Note labour cost to farmer also includes Social Security payments. Allowance has to be made for labour used to grow forage as well as to look after the cows.
† £65 depreciation, £50 repairs and contract, £40 fuel & electricity, £5 licences/insurances.
‡ Includes accountancy/professional fees, office expenses and general insurance.

Margin over Concentrates (MoC)
The data is also set out in such a way as to bring together the factors that are interrelated. The most significant sets of data are those relating to milk sales and concentrate feed costs. Together these determine the 'Margin over Concentrates'. Some farmers

purchase feed such as brewers' grains as an alternative to concentrates. The cost of these feeds should be included as part of concentrate feed costs, i.e. they should be treated as concentrate equivalents if the margin over concentrate efficiency measure is to have a meaningful value.

The budget margin over concentrates, or MoC for short, at 1980–1 prices is £400 or 5000 litres at 8·0p margin per litre, but this is only an 'average' figure. The actual margins achieved by farmers will vary enormously around this figure ranging from £300 to over £500 per cow. Considerable argument and discussion surrounds the question of how best to achieve a good MoC but survey after survey shows that high yields are necessary to achieve the highest margins. Good margins can be achieved, however, at modest yield levels if grassland management is above average and providing this is coupled with a very careful control of feed costs.

In seeking to achieve a high MoC a farmer has basically to choose between three solutions. These are (1) to increase the yield without commensurate increases in feed costs, (2) to reduce feed costs without commensurate reductions in yield, or (3) to increase yields and reduce feed costs at the same time. The latter may seem impossible but in practice some high-yielding herds do achieve these yields with lower than average concentrate feed costs. This is due to their ability to combine above-average stockmanship resulting in good yields with above-average grassmanship resulting in good-quality grazing and bulk foods. It is a pity that over the years there has been much conflict between the exponents of good grassmanship and the need to reduce concentrate costs. The most successful farmers are those with the ability to combine both facets in their management strategy.

The difficulty and feasibility of the alternative approaches to the problem of achieving a high MoC are shown in Table 18.9. The reader is asked to look at this table and try to draw his own conclusions bearing in mind that 0·123p is equivalent to approximately 0·1 kg per litre.

Table 18.9 assumes a milk price of 12·0 pence per litre. Improving the milk price is an alternative method of trying to improve the margin. As mentioned previously this aspect may become of increasing significance in the future but this factor to date has been of secondary importance compared to the need to attain high yields.

When assessing the MoC obtained on a particular farm it is necessary to also take into account the stocking rate, together with level of expenditure on forage costs, and fixed costs associated with the production of the forage. This is an exercise requiring

Table 18.9. Feed Cost per litre if milk price is 12·0p

Yield/output (litres)	MoC (£)	£400 (pence)	£450 (pence)	£500 (pence)	£550 (pence)	£600 (pence)
4500	540	3·11	2·00	0·89	NF*	NF*
5000	600	4·00	3·00	2·00	1·00	Nil
5500	660	4·72	3·82	2·91	2·00	1·09
6000	720	5·33	4·50	3·67	2·83	2·00
6500	780	5·85	5·08	4·30	3·54	2·77

* NF—Not Feasible: milk sales less than MoC

considerable knowledge and experience in farm business management and costings, and there is not sufficient space to allow all these aspects to be covered in this chapter.

It is necessary, however, to emphasise the significance of MoC as an efficiency measure in dairy farming. In turn this leads to a need to underline the main factors resulting in a good yield and a good margin. Foremost among these is the quality of grazing and bulk feed available on the farm. Not only does this keep down feed costs, it also facilitates the attainment of good yields.

The various factors determining milk yield and efficiency of grassland and forage utilisation have been detailed elsewhere in this book. The attainment of good margins depends largely on how well these factors are controlled and implemented on the farm. Mention has been made elsewhere of various recording systems and again this is considered a vital factor determining the level of margin attained. All dairy farmers should monitor carefully their yields and feed inputs in both physical and economic terms.

Returns per Hectare
Emphasis up to now has been placed on margins per cow rather than per hectare. This is considered justified as the capital invested in a dairy farm tends to be closely related to the number of cows. Consequently high margins per cow tend to be associated with high returns to capital.

A large proportion of dairy herds, however, are on small farms, and on small farms land is the most limiting factor and consequently return per hectare becomes more important than return per cow. The stocking rate in this context becomes a most important factor. The most successful dairy farmers achieve not only higher margins per cow but manage to achieve this at higher stocking rates. This is illustrated in Table 18.10. Note that the expenditure on concentrates and forage has been purposely set at the same level for the above average as for the average farmer. The secret of the above average farmer's success is that he achieves a greater output for the same level of inputs. This applies whether the inputs are feed or fertilisers, and is a reflection of his increased managerial skill and ability to do things at the right time. Silage quality, for example, is not determined by the amount of fertiliser used but on the ability to cut and conserve grass at the right stage of growth together with the appropriate degree of wilting and consolidation.

Table 18.10. Stocking Rates and Margins per Cow

	Average £	Above average £
Results per Cow		
Milk sales	5000 litres @ 12p–600	5500 @ 12p–660
Concentrate feed costs	5000 litres @ 4p–200	5500 @ 3·6p–200
Margin over concentrates	5000 litres @ 8p–400	5500 @ 8·4p–460
Forage costs	0·5 ha @ £120–60	0·45 ha @ £120–54
Margin over concentrate and forage costs	340	406
Results per Hectare		
No. cows per hectare	2·0	2·2
Margin over concentrate and forage costs per hectare	680	893

This ability to do things at the right time and by the correct methods has a very marked effect on the profitability of dairy farming. Not only do the best farmers achieve higher yields and stocking rates from given feed and fertiliser inputs, but they also achieve these with no greater expenditure on labour and machinery. Consequently these are the farmers who have the ability to pay high rent or service high-rent equivalents in the form of finance charges.

This is illustrated in the Table 18.11. By making better use of the resources the above-average farmer achieves an increase in the profit before rent and finance charges of £140 per hectare, 60 per cent more than average. This allows him to service a well-above-average rent charge and still make an above-average management and investment income.

In Table 18.11 it will be noticed that little difference has been assumed between the above-average and average farm in terms of calf values and herd maintenance costs.

As mentioned previously, calf values have a very significant effect on the fortunes of dairy farming from year to year but they account for very little of the difference in profit between farms. This is not to minimise the importance of avoiding calf mortality and trying to get as good a market value for calves as is possible.

Note. The above points are made in relation to the national herd which is largely dominated by the Friesian and Canadian Holstein breeds. Significant differences do occur when comparing Friesian herds to Channel Island herds but that is not the point being made in this section. This lack of good calf output is a point that has to be carefully considered when making the decision whether or not to go for 'milk yield or quality'.

Table 18.11. Stocking Rates and Profits

		Average £s per cow		Above average £s per cow
Margin over concentrates		400		460
Calf value		45		50
		445		510
Herd maintenance costs	35		30	
Vet and sundry costs	35	70	35	65
Gross margin before forage		375		445
Forage costs		60		60
Gross Margin		315		385
		Per hectare		Per hectare
No. cows		2·0		2·2
Gross margin		630		770
Fixed Costs				
Labour		200		200
Power & machinery		160		160
Sundry overheads		40		40
		400		400
Profit before Rent, Finance and Management Charges		230		370
Rent		60		say 100
Management and Investment Income		170		270

Herd Maintenance Costs

Herd maintenance costs at first glance do not appear to be a very significant factor determining the difference in profits between farms; a difference of only £5 per cow, for example, has been shown in Table 18.11.

A word of explanation is perhaps necessary concerning the term 'herd maintenance costs'. How this is determined is illustrated in Table 18.12. It represents the difference between the value received for cows culled from the herd and the cost or market value of their replacements.

Table 18.12. Herd Maintenance Cost

Heifers purchased	10 @ £475 =	£4,750
Heifers reared (market value)	12 @ £475 =	£5,700
	22 @ £475 =	£10,450
Cows culled	20 @ £360 =	£7,200
Casualties	2 @ £10 =	£20
	22 @ £328 =	£7,220
Herd maintenance cost		£3,230
No. of Cows in Herd		100
Herd maintenance cost per cow		£32·30

As can be seen from Table 18.12 the herd maintenance cost is due to basically two factors, i.e. the number or percentage of the herd culled and the difference between the cull price and the purchase price of the replacements.

Most cows are culled either because they cannot be got in-calf or because of disease or ill-health, e.g. mastitis, and a high culling rate is often associated with poor performance in terms of yields and MoC.

Generally speaking it is difficult to justify culling for yield unless the yield of the cow to be culled is exceptionally low. It takes a long time to recover the £140–£150 it normally costs to replace a cow. To get this money back in two years the replacement animals needs to produce an additional £70–£75 MoC per annum.

If the culling rate is high this can lead to the need for an above-average number of dairy followers on the farm.

This is not desirable as the rearing of dairy heifers is relatively unprofitable compared to milk production both from a return per hectare and a return on capital point of view. Dairy heifer rearing is also less profitable than cereal growing where conditions are suitable for cereals. An important factor in the economy of the whole farm, therefore, is the number of dairy followers relative to dairy cows. Generally speaking they should not exceed two-thirds of cow numbers unless there are special reasons for their being kept, such as fields which are inaccessible for grazing by dairy cows and are also unsuitable for cereals.

For more detail of the factors summarised in this chapter readers are referred to *Dairy Farm Business Management* by Slater and Throup, published by Farming Press.

CHAPTER 19

STARTING A DAIRY HERD

FINANCIAL success in any dairying enterprise depends, to a large degree, on the wise investment of capital, principally in good, productive cows.

The question is, how are those good cows to be obtained? The short and easy answer is by breeding: but what of the foundation stock—how does one start from scratch?

ADVICE TO A YOUNG MAN

Where ample capital is available, price is not a limiting factor. High-yielding cattle, with impressive milk records and pedigrees, can be bought at special sales sponsored by the respective breed societies, or at draft or dispersal sales from well-known herds. In this way a high-yielding herd can quickly be established.

But the continuation of this high production will depend on maintaining the highly skilled system of management and breeding carried out by the vendors.

High prices are no guarantee of success, and the newcomer to dairying, lacking both capital and experience, would be extremely foolish to risk his capital in this manner.

I would advise the young man starting a dairy herd, and with his farming life ahead of him, to buy honest, useful-looking cattle as cheaply as possible. Then, as experience and skill in management are gained, let him cull hard.

The main deterrent to culling is the fear of capital depreciation. But, without culling, breeding progress will be slow and the burden of low-yielders will reduce the profitability of the herd as a whole. As a guide for a young farmer I would set out the following points:

1. Remember the need for an adequate build-up of food reserves and for a certain minimum standard of buildings and equipment to conform to the Milk and Dairies Regulations. When occupying

271

a new farm, work out a suitable cropping programme to meet the needs of the dairy herd, and then get the buildings prepared for milk production.

During this initial period, the maximum area of cash crops should be grown in order to provide income while the herd is being built up.

2. Aim from the outset to establish a herd free of disease. If buying cattle at an auction, study the auction rules in regard to any warranty given when cattle are sold.

3. If you can, buy bulling heifers that have been bred in a good herd where the dams, sire, and half-sisters can be seen. In this way you stand as good a chance as the vendor in selecting the best animals; whereas, with older cattle already in milk, the advantage lies entirely with the seller.

4. Where capital resources are low, the purchase of non-pedigree cattle is recommended, preferably sired by pedigree bulls. The selection is wider with non-pedigree cattle and prices are generally lower. And, provided a buyer selects his purchases with skill, he is likely to buy as productive cattle as if he buys pedigree. The pedigree breeder rarely sells his best cattle.

5. As a policy for the future, aim at grading-up to full pedigree status. This is a way to accumulate capital reserves; the herd becomes an appreciating asset.

BUYING STOCK FOR A FLYING HERD

On small, heavily stocked, high-rent farms, circumstances may make it impossible to run a self-contained herd.

In such circumstances the purchase of reliable replacements is quite a problem. To make a success of a flying herd the owner must be a very shrewd judge of a cow.

Some dairy farmers possess this ability; they can buy just as good cattle as they are likely to breed and rear. If they use AI on their cows and are able to arrange to have their heifer calves reared elsewhere, with a view to repurchase as down-calvers, many of the risks associated with flying herds would be eliminated.

Such schemes would aid the flying herd areas of the industrial North notably East Lancashire and the West Riding of Yorkshire.

The importance of subsidiary enterprises on a dairy farm has already been stressed, both from the point of view of making full use of farm labour and of intensifying production to increase the overall farm income.

Pigs on Dairy Farms

The most likely enterprise to be adopted is pig production, but if it is to fit in well with the dairy herd, the system adopted needs to have certain characteristics:

1. It should be intensive, so that the work involved is indoors. Pig fattening would be suitable.

2. Feeding should be as far as possible on the self-feeding basis so that the bulk of the work can be done between milking times. Feeding hoppers can be refilled in the late morning or early afternoon without the pigs having to wait for their food.

On farms too small to be organised into specialised full-time labour units of cows and pigs it is only by such integration of labour resources that high output per man can be achieved.

Beef Production

As an enterprise, production of 18-months-old beef, either fattened indoors on silage and barley or fattened off grass, could compete with dairy cows for buildings and land resources. The gross margin for such an enterprise is likely to be much lower than for milk production but, on some farms, buildings and land not suitable for milk production may well be used for this form of beef production, or for intensive beef where buildings are available on arable farms.

The majority of dairy farmers today have specialised to such a degree that beef production has given place to intensified dairying. Such farmers sell their surplus calves for beef production, through the market or calf selling groups, to specialist calf rearers or beef producers.

The importance of the 'second income' accruing to dairy farmers from sale of calves influences policy as to the breed of cow kept and whether to breed herd replacements. Given reasonable fertility in the cows and a herd life of four to five lactations, up to 40 per cent of a herd and all the first-calf heifers can be mated to beef bulls, rearing pure-bred replacements from the remaining 60 per cent.

Demand for calves is likely to remain keen to increase beef production in this country. Reduction of calf mortality, which causes 7 to 10 per cent of annual losses, should be every dairy farmer's aim in the short term. E. Coli infections and Salmonellosis are the chief causes of losses in young calves, and respiratory (virus) infection in intensively-reared calves later in life.

When Beef Will Pay

Therefore, on dairy farms, beef production is most likely to find a place where:

1. Cows are kept which will give good-class beef calves if crossed with a pure beef bull (as can be done under the AI service.) These calves can be sold at very favourable prices, or they can be reared at home provided there is sufficient keep available which is not required by the dairy herd.

Such an extension of home rearing would enable large farms to be more fully stocked without the capital expenditure that would be needed to establish a second dairy herd and without requiring extra labour.

2. Where dairy heifers are reared for sale the possibility of using a beef bull—Aberdeen Angus, for instance—on each year's crop of bulling heifers and rearing the progeny for beef is worth considering. The dairy herd replacements would then be bred from the cows only.

3. On some mainly-grass dairy farms on rich vale land, off-lying fields inaccessible to the dairy herd may be grazed with beef cattle bought in as strong stores. Where there is an appreciable acreage of such land beef calves can be reared and finished on the farm.

SHEEP ON DAIRY FARMS

Any expected expansion in lamb and mutton production will, in the main, have to come from lowland farms. I believe that on dairy farms sheep can profitably be fitted to the farm in one of two ways.

A dry flock of lambs, bought in the autumn, can act as grassland scavengers during the winter. If practicable, such lambs should be finished and sold off fat by mid-January.

If given some trough food or grazed on catch crops, such as rape or Italian ryegrass and trefoil, this will allow pasture to recover without heavy spring grazing which would compete with the needs of the dairy herd.

Three or four lambs per hectare of total grazing, including catch crops, will probably be required. Such a flock would add to the farm income without any appreciable addition to labour or other expenses.

Where dairying is less intensive and where more off-lying grazing is available, a flying flock of ewes of a grass type, for example Kerry Hill of Half-Bred, can be run. One ewe per young beast being reared is a useful guide as to the stocking rate.

Run mainly as scavengers, with lambing down in March or early April, such ewes require little supplementary feeding other than grass. If four-year-old or five-year-old ewes are bought, lambing should present few problems, even to relatively unskilled labour.

Advantage of Mixed Stocking
These ewes and their lambs will provide most useful supplementary grazing to the young cattle on the farm, or else they can be used as scavengers behind the dairy herd itself.

Mixed stocking with sheep and cattle does raise the total output from grazing and also helps to maintain the desired balance of grass to clover in a sward.

On many farms there may be difficulties in keeping sheep. In some areas the dog menace is a very real one, and fencing can also be a problem; but from the point of profitability and in raising total farm revenue without heavy expenditure, sheep undoubtedly merit a place in the economy of many dairy farms.

THE OUTLOOK FOR MILK PRODUCTION

In the past twenty-five years, the numbers of milk producers has dropped in England and Wales from 142,792 in 1955, to 43,358 in 1980. Annual milk yield per cow has risen from 3065 litres per cow to 4810 litres per cow (*Dairy Facts and Figures*).

On the farm this means that there has been a considerable trend towards increasing specialisation in milk production with larger and more efficient units.

Mechanisation of dairying has gone hand in hand with cereal growing. Yield can be expected to increase in terms of the national average but the profit margins are increasingly going to be concerned with the balance between level of milk price, concentrate prices and cost of fertilisers. Fixed costs will also continue to rise and will exert increasing pressures on every dairy farm. Good economic yields per cow coupled with better grassland management, resulting in tighter stocking rates, are the only ways in which dairy farms of the future can hope to survive as economic units.

Through the marketing boards, active sales campaigns for both liquid milk and dairy products are continually being put into operation.

Further capital investment in plant and equipment to deal with seasonal surpluses is planned, with continued market research to anticipate and meet changes in consumer demand. The establishment of a national minimum standard of hygienic quality and the grading of milk on its compositional quality (particularly in respect of its s.n.f. percentage) has been achieved.

The milk industry has seen a technological revolution since the Second World War. The upsurge in technical efficiency has exceeded any increase in liquid consumption by probably 5 per cent per annum.

On the larger farms expansion in herd size has gone on apace, threatening the livelihood of milk producers on the smaller farms where further expansion by intensification is particularly difficult. On social grounds many of these small owner-occupied farms represent a stable element in the countryside. Their future in dairying, or any other form of production which benefits from increasing scale of enterprise, may well not be spelt out in strictly economic terms.

Confidence in the future of milk production is necessary to support the very heavy capital investment needed today, in cows and equipment alone of the order of possibly £1,500–£2,500 per hectare depending upon system.

Such a level of capital investment imposes on dairy farmers a reluctance to change which does not apply to the same extent with other types of farming such as beef or sheep production. Investment in stock with beef may be as high per hectare, but fixed equipment costs are notably less.

There would seem to be a very definite place for co-operation among small milk producers, particularly in the formation of machinery syndicates to secure the advantages of modern conservation processes such as silage and 'quick' haymaking and of bulk buying of feeding stuffs to reduce delivery and transport costs.

For good stockmanship there is no substitute, and provided the small dairy farmer is prepared to deny himself the mass-inspired worship of the five-day week, he will be able to face the future with confidence with such improvements to the organisation of his farming.

With the larger dairy farmer, the greatest problem is not likely to be in the economic field so much as in the field of personal relationship with his dairy employees. We speak of the one-man unit which is, of course, not strictly true—who is to be the relief milker? In all but the largest herds employing at least three men, relief milking will be the farmer's responsibility or that of his family.

The last advice I would give to a young man starting dairy farming is, therefore, be prepared to accept the discipline the dairy cow will invariably impose on your private life.

APPENDICES

Appendix 1

1. BREED COMPARISON ACCORDING TO MILK YIELDS (ENGLAND AND WALES)

Five main breeds	Milk Yield (lactation averages) 1956–7 Average yield kg	1978–9 Average yield kg
Ayrshire	3,094	4,863
Dairy Shorthorn	3,583	4,730
Friesian	4,443	5,441
Guernsey	3,467	3,941
Jersey	3,275	3,776
All breeds*	3,984	5,335

* Includes all other breeds

2. BREED COMPARISON ACCORDING TO BUTTERFAT

Five main breeds	Average percentage butterfat 1956–7 % Fat	1978–9 % Fat
Ayrshire	3·85	3·94
Dairy Shorthorn	3·56	3·62
Friesian	3·55	3·79
Guernsey	4·55	4·65
Jersey	5·02	5·14
All breeds*	3·85	3·83

* Includes all other breeds
Source: U.K. *Dairy Facts and Figures*, 1980, MMB.

277

Appendix II

CALCULATIONS FOR ESTIMATING WEIGHTS OF CONTENTS OF SILOS,
STACKS, ETC.

Stacks of Hay and Straw

First, work out the cubic capacity of the stack.

For rectangular stacks multiply length by breadth (in metres) and multiply that figure by height to eaves. Then add cubic capacity of roof—obtained by multiplying the length by breadth again and multiplying that figure by half the height of the roof, measured perpendicularly from eaves to ridge.

For round stacks, square the circumference, multiply by 0·08 and then multiply by a figure equal to the height to the eaves plus one-third of the height of the roof, measured perpendicularly from the eaves to the peak. All measurements should be made in metres.

When the total cubic capacity is known, tonnage can be worked out from the following tables:

AVERAGE NUMBER OF CUBIC METRES PER TONNE OF HAY

Condition of stack	Square stacks	Round stacks
	m^3 per tonne	
Not well settled	9·0	9·8
Fairly well settled	7·5	8·3
Very well settled	6·0	6·8

AVERAGE NUMBER OF CUBIC METRES PER TONNE OF STRAW

	m^3 per tonne
Wheat straw	13·5–15·0
Oat straw	15·0–17·3
Barley straw	15·0–17·3

Roots

The average weight per cubic metre of roots in clamp is: Fodderbeet 545 kg, Swedes 545 kg, Mangolds 561 kg.

Pit Silos

Work out the cubic capacity in metres—multiply length by breadth by height, taking average measurements—then reckon that each cubic metre weighs 0·664 tonne.

Tower Silos

The weight of silage per cubic metre is variable, depending on the depth of silage, diameter of silo, fineness of cutting, packing, etc., but on an average 1 cubic metre equals 664 kg.

Height of silo m	Average weight of silage kg/m³	Capacity of silo in tonnes when diameter of silo in metres			
		3	4	5	6
7·92	596	37	—	—	—
8·53	615	41	74	—	—
9·14	635	46	81	—	—
9·75	652	50	90	—	—
10·36	670	55	97	153	—
10·97	686	—	106	166	238
11·58	702	—	—	178	258
12·19	718	—	—	192	277
12·80	732	—	—	206	297
13·41	749	—	—	221	317
14·02	758	—	—	234	337
14·63	769	—	—	247	356
15·24	782	—	—	262	377

Appendix III

ANALYSES AND FEEDING VALUE OF COMPOUND FEEDS

Feeding Stuff	Analysis per cent by weight			Approximate nutritive value	
	Oil	Crude Protein	Fibre no more than	g/kg DM DCP	MJ/kg DM ME
Dairy Nuts 0·4 kg/litre	3–5	14–18	8	130–175	12·4–12·9
Dairy Nuts 0·35 kg/litre	4–5·5	14–18	7	130–175	13·2–13·8
Dairy Nuts 0·3 kg/litre	6–8	15–21	5	140–200	14–14·4
High Protein Balancer	3–6	34–38	8	300–330	11·5–12·5

Appendix IV

FOOD VALUES*

1. Home-Grown Concentrates

					DM g/kg	ME DM MJ/kg	DCP DM g/kg
Beans	...	...	...	...	860	12·8	209–248
Peas ...	...	...	...	...	860	13·4	225
Linseed	...	...	...	...	900	19·3	208
Dried grass							
29% crude protein or over			...	900	10·8	*113
16%–19% crude protein	...		...	900	10·6	†136
12%–15% crude protein	...		...	900	9·7	§97
Wheat	...	...	...	...	860	14·0	105
Oats ...	...	...	...	...	860	11·5	84
Barley	...	...	...	...	860	13·7	82
Sugar-beet pulp (dry)		...	...	900	12·7	59

* v. leafy † leafy § in flower

II. Purchased Concentrates

				DM g/kg	ME DM MJ/kg	DCP DM g/kg
White Fishmeal	...	...	...	900	11·1	631
Decorticated Groundnut Cake		...	900	12·9	449
Dried Yeast ...	...	...	...	900	11·7	381
Soya Bean Cake	...	...	...	900	13·3	454
Decorticated Cottonseed Cake		...	900	12·3	393
High Protein Cake	...	...		—	—	—
Undecorticated Groundnut Cake		...	900	11·4	310
Linseed Cake	...	...	...	900	13·4	286
Grain Balancer Cake	...	...		—	—	—
Maize Gluten Feed	...	...	...	900	13·5	223
Dried Distillers' Grains	...	...	900	12·1	214
Sunflower Seed Cake	...	...	900	13·3	372
Undecorticated Cottonseed Cake		...	900	8·7	203
Palm Kernel Cake	...	...	...	900	12·8	196
Coconut Cake	...	...	...	900	13·0	184
Malt Culms ...	...	...	...	900	11·2	222
Dried Brewers' Grains	...	...	900	10·3	145

* Now expressed as Metabolisable Energy (MJ/kg DM), Disgestable Crude Protein (g/kg DM and Dry Matter (g/kg). See MAFF Bulletin No. 33.

Appendix IV (continued)

Purchased Concentrates

continued

				DM g/kg	ME DM MJ/kg	DCP DM g/kg
Typical Dairy Cake	...	...	...	—	—	—
Weatings	...	...	...	880	11·9	129
Bran	...	...	...	880	10·1	126
Maize Germ Meal	...	...	...	900	13·2	90
Maize Meal or Flaked	...	...	900	15·6	99
Locust Beans	...	...	...	860	13·8	47
Molasses	...	...	...	750	12·9	16
Tapioca Meal	...	...	...	900	15·0	13

III. Succulents

				DM g/kg	ME DM MJ/kg	DCP DM g/kg
Cabbage	...	...	...	...	110	10·4	100
Kale ...	...	...	...	...	140	11·0	123
Rape	...	...	...	...	140	9·5	144
Beet tops	...	...	...	...	160	9·9	88
Mangolds	...	...	...	...	120	12·4	58
Swedes	...	...	...	...	120	12·8	91
Grass silage	...	...	...	...	220	7·6–10·2	98–116
Maize silage ...	...	...	...	210	10·8	70
Pasture grass (4″ stage)	...	...	200	12·2	225
Pasture grass (8″ stage)	...	...	200	11·2	130
Pasture grass (mature)	...	...	200	10·0	124
Fodder beet (Pajbjerg Rex X)	...	—	—	—
Wet Grains	...	...	...	...	220	10·0	149
Wet Beet Pulp	...	...	...	180	12·7	66

IV. Roughages

				DM g/kg	ME DM MJ/kg	DCP DM g/kg
Hay, very good, leafy	...	...	850	10·1	90
Seeds hay, medium	...	...	...	850	8·9	103
Meadow hay, poor	...	...	...	850	7·5	45
Lucerne hay ...	...	...	...	850	8·2	166
Straws:						
Oat	...	...	...	...	860	6·7	11
Barley	...	...	...	...	860	7·3	9
Wheat cavings	...	...	...	860	5·9	13
Bean and pea haulm	...	...	860	7·4	26

Appendix V

TABLE FOR USE IN CALCULATING WINTER RATIONS
Amounts available per head over—

Quantity available	3 months (91 days)	4 months (121 days)	5 months (152 days)	6 months (182 days)
(kg)	(kg)	(kg)	(kg)	(kg)
250	2·7	2·1	1·6	1·4
300	3·3	2·5	2·0	1·6
350	3·8	2·9	2·3	1·9
400	4·4	3·3	2·6	2·2
450	4·9	3·7	3·0	2·5
500	5·5	4·1	3·3	2·7
600	6·6	5·0	3·9	3·3
700	7·6	5·8	4·6	3·8
800	8·8	6·6	5·3	4·4
900	9·9	7·4	5·9	4·9
1,000	11·0	8·3	6·6	5·5
1,500	16·5	12·4	9·9	8·2
2,000	22·0	16·5	13·2	11·0
2,500	27·5	20·7	16·4	13·7
3,000	33·0	24·8	19·7	16·5
4,000	44·0	33·1	26·3	22·0
5,000	54·9	41·3	32·9	27·5

INDEX

Untreated milk, 37
Urea supplements, use of, 235
Urine colour, 243
Utilisation of milk, 255

Vacuum, milking machine, 179
Vices, in dairy cows, 192
—, kicking, 192
—, suckling, 197
Vitamin D, 138
Vitamin deficiencies, 138
Vitamins, 138

Warble fly control, 251
Washing procedures, 40
—, acid boiling water, 40
—, circulation cleaning, 40
Weaning, of calves, 227

—, feeding after, 232
Weather service, for farmers, 110
Wholesale producers, 17
Wilting, value of, 167
Winter feed requirements, hay, 140
—, on grass farm, 141
—, on mixed arable farm, 142
Winter rations, examples, 147
Work routines, parlours, 76

Yard and parlour system, 54
—, advantages of, 63
—, yard lay-out, 63
Yellow body, 247
Young stock at grass, 233

Zero-grazing system, 156